# Bond

# Maths
## Assessment Papers

## 10–11+ years
## Book 2

### David Clemson

Nelson Thornes

Published in 2011 by:
Nelson Thornes Ltd
Delta Place
27 Bath Road
CHELTENHAM
GL53 7TH
United Kingdom

13 14 / 10 9 8 7 6 5 4 3

A catalogue record for this book is available from the British Library

ISBN 978 1 4085 1694 2

Page make-up by Tech-Set Ltd, Gateshead

Printed in China by 1010 Printing International Ltd

# Before you get started

## What is Bond?

This book is part of the Bond Assessment Papers series for maths, which provides **thorough and continuous practice of all the key maths content** from ages five to thirteen. Bond's maths resources are ideal preparation for many different kinds of tests and exams – from SATs to 11+ and other secondary school selection exams.

## How does the scope of this book match real exam content?

*Maths 10-11+ Book 1* and *Book 2* are the core Bond 11+ books. Each paper is **pitched at the level of a typical 11+ exam** and covers the key maths a child would be expected to learn. The papers are also in line with other selective exams for this age group. The coverage is matched to the National Curriculum and the National Numeracy Strategy and will also **provide invaluable preparation for Key Stage 2 SATs**. One of the key features of Bond Assessment Papers is that each one practises **a wide variety of skills and question types** so that children are always challenged to think – and don't get bored repeating the same question type again and again. We think that variety is the key to effective learning. It helps children 'think on their feet' and cope with the unexpected.

## What does the book contain?

- **21 papers** – each one contains 50 questions.
- **Tutorial links throughout** – B 5 – this icon appears in the margin next to the questions. It indicates links to the relevant section in *How to do ... 11+ Maths*, our invaluable subject guide that offers explanations and practice for all core question types.
- **Scoring devices** – there are score boxes in the margins and a progress chart on page 68. The chart is a visual and motivating way for children to see how they are doing. It also turns the score into a percentage that can help decide what to do next.
- **Next Steps Planner** – advice on what to do after finishing the papers can be found on the inside back cover.
- **Answers** – located in an easily-removed central pull-out section.

## How can you use this book?

One of the great strengths of Bond Assessment Papers is their flexibility. They can be used at home, in school and by tutors to:

- set **timed formal practice** tests – allow about 30 minutes per paper in line with standard 11+ demands. Reduce the suggested time limit by five minutes to practise working at speed.

- provide **bite-sized chunks** for regular practice.
- **highlight strengths and weaknesses** in the core skills.
- identify **individual needs**.
- set **homework**.
- follow **a complete 11+ preparation strategy** alongside *The Parents' Guide to the 11+* (see below).

It is best to start at the beginning and work through the papers in order. Calculators should not be used.

Remind children to check whether each answer needs a unit of measurement before they start a test. If units of measurement are not included in answers that require them, they will lose marks for those questions. To ensure that children can practise including them in their answers, units of measurement have been omitted after the answer rules for some questions.

If you are using the book as part of a careful run-in to the 11+, we suggest that you also have two other essential Bond resources close at hand:

*How to do ... 11+ Maths*: the subject guide that explains all the question types practised in this book. Use the cross-reference icons to find the relevant sections.

*The Parents' Guide to the 11+*: the step-by-step guide to the whole 11+ experience. It clearly explains the 11+ process, provides guidance on how to assess children, helps you to set complete action plans for practice and explains how you can use the *Fourth* and *Maths 10-11+ Book 1* and *Book 2* as part of a strategic run-in to the exam.

See the inside front cover for more details of these books.

## What does a score mean and how can it be improved?

It is unfortunately impossible to guarantee that a child will pass the 11+ exam if they achieve a certain score on any practice book or paper. Success on the day depends on a host of factors, including the scores of the other children sitting the test. However, we can give some guidance on what a score indicates and how to improve it.

If children colour in the progress chart on page 68, this will give an idea of present performance in percentage terms. The Next Steps Planner inside the back cover will help you to decide what to do next to help a child progress. It is always valuable to go over wrong answers with children. If they are having trouble with any particular question type, follow the tutorial links to *How to do ... 11+ Maths* for step-by-step explanations and further practice.

## *Free Papers on the Internet.*

This book should contain 24 papers, in line with *Maths 10-11+ Book 1*. As it has only been possible to fit 21 papers into this book, Papers 22–24 are free to download via the 'Additional Resources' link on the Bond website. (See below for website details). The answers to Papers 22–24 can be found on pages A7–8 of the central pull-out section.

## *Don't forget the website...!*

Visit www.bond11plus.co.uk for lots of advice, information and suggestions on everything to do with Bond, the 11+ and helping children to do their best.

# Key words

Some special maths words are used in this book. You will find them **in bold** each time they appear in the papers. These words are explained here.

**acute angle**  an angle that is less than a right angle

**coordinates**  the two numbers, the first horizontal the second vertical, that plot a point on a grid, e.g. (3, 2)

**factor**  the factors of a number are numbers that divide into it, e.g. 1, 2, 4 and 8 are all factors of 8

**kite**  a four-sided shape that looks like a stretched diamond

**lowest term**  the simplest you can make a fraction, e.g. $\frac{4}{10}$ reduced to the lowest term is $\frac{2}{5}$

**mean**  one kind of average. You find the mean by adding all the scores together and dividing by the number of scores, e.g. the mean of 1, 3 and 8 is 4

**median**  one kind of average. The middle number of a set of numbers after being ordered from lowest to highest, e.g. the median of 1, 3 and 8 is 3

**mixed number**  a number that contains a whole number and a fraction, e.g. $5\frac{1}{2}$ is a mixed number

**mode**  one kind of average. The most common number in a set of numbers, e.g. the mode of 2, 3, 2, 7, 2 is 2

**obtuse angle**  an angle that is more than 90° and not more than 180°

**parallelogram**  a four-sided shape that has all its opposite sides equal and parallel

**polygon**  a closed shape with three or more sides

**prime factor**  the factors of a number that are also prime numbers, e.g. the prime factors of 12 are 2 and 3

**prime number**  any number that can only be divided by itself or 1. 2, 3 and 7 are prime numbers. (Note that 1 is not a prime number.)

**quotient**  the answer if you divide one number by another, e.g. the quotient of 12 ÷ 4 is 3

**range**  the difference between the largest and smallest of a set of numbers, e.g. the range of 1, 2, 5, 3, 6, 8 is 7

**reflex angle**  an angle that is bigger than 180° and less than 360°

**rhombus**  a four-sided shape, like a squashed square, that has all its sides of equal length and its opposite sides parallel

**trapezium**  a four-sided shape that has just one pair of parallel sides

**vertex, vertices**  the point where two or more edges or sides in a shape meet

## Paper 1

Write these in figures.

**1** two hundred thousand and twenty

**2** forty-nine thousand and forty-nine

A map uses a scale of 1:100 000.

**3** If a road is 5 km long, how long will it be on the map?   _____ cm

Put the appropriate signs in these calculations to make them correct.

**4** 102 __ 6 = 17          **5** 48 __ 4 = 12          **6** 4 __ (9 × 8) = 76

**7** (8 × 12) __ 5 = 91          **8** 12 + (8 __ 3) = 17          **9–10** (11 __ 6) × 9 = 45

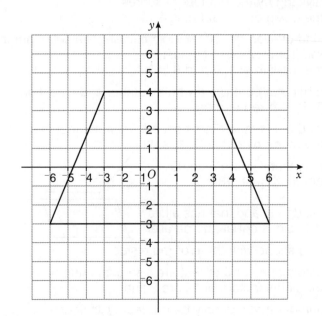

Write the **coordinates** of this shape.

**11–14** ( __ , __ ) ( __ , __ ) ( __ , __ ) ( __ , __ )

**15** What is the name of the shape above?   _____

**16** What is the perimeter of the shape?   _____ cm

**17** What is the area of the shape?   _____ cm²

Circle the smallest in each of these groups.

**18**   $\frac{1}{3}$ of 8      $\frac{2}{3}$ of 12      $\frac{1}{2}$ of 14      $\frac{3}{4}$ of 16      $\frac{3}{5}$ of 15

**19**        $\frac{5}{8}$           $\frac{1}{2}$           $\frac{1}{6}$           $\frac{2}{8}$           $\frac{3}{8}$

**20**       $\frac{17}{40}$          $\frac{40}{40}$          $\frac{8}{10}$           $\frac{4}{5}$           $\frac{35}{50}$

**21**   0.33        $\frac{2}{3}$           $\frac{5}{6}$        0.4           $\frac{1}{4}$

**22**   507      0.507      50.7      0.0507      5.07

B 10
B 11

5

B 14
B 10
B 12
B 2
B 3

6

B 15

6

B 9

4

B 8
1

B 1
1

A local football club did a survey of 96 of their spectators.

They drew this pie chart showing the age ranges of these fans.

**23**  What fraction is in the age range 28–38?  _____

**24**  What fraction is in the age range 6–16?  _____

**25**  What percentage is in the age range 39–49?  _____

**26**  How many spectators are over 16?  _____

**27**  How many 6–27-year-olds are there?  _____

**28**  How many spectators are not aged between 17 and 49?  _____

Write the **mode**, **median** and **mean** of these sets of numbers.

**29–31**  10      5      6      8      6

The mode is _____      The median is _____      The mean is _____

**32–34**  12      15      19      18      15      22      25

The mode is _____      The median is _____      The mean is _____

**35–38**  Write down the numbers that will come out of this machine.

15   24   36   47      ×10      −3

**39**  Kamal buys his lunches Monday to Friday and they cost £p per day. He buys lunch on the weekends for £q per day. Expressed as an equation, how much does Kamal spend each week on lunch?  _____

**40**  Multiply 10.06 by 10.  _____

3

Divide these by 100 to give a **quotient**.

**41** 265 _____

**42** 138.8 _____

**43** 406.15 _____

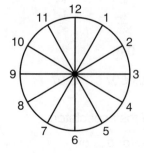

What is the size of the smaller angle between:

**44** 2 and 4? _____°

**45** 4 and 9? _____°

**46** 9 and 10? _____°

**47** 8 and 12? _____°

Between them Anish, Jason and Rob have 40 swap cards. Jason has twice as many as Anish, and Rob has five times as many as Anish.

**48** How many does Anish have? _____

**49** How many does Jason have? _____

**50** How many does Rob have? _____

*Now go to the Progress Chart to record your score!*     Total    50

# Paper 2

**1–4**    Solve these calculations.

```
  458        423                        337
  394      ×   8        _____       ×  45
+ 825                 13)2873
  _____      _____                      _____
```

Multiply these by 100.

**5** 56.15 _____     **6** 13.06 _____     **7** 0.107 _____

Divide these by 100.

**8** 3126 _____     **9** 458.5 _____     **10** 11.73 _____

START

FINISH
Red Route

FINISH
Green Route

**11–12** The robot is on START. Guide it along the two routes shown above to reach the FINISH. It can only move Forward, Turn Right 90° and Turn Left 90°. Circle one letter (A, B, C, D, E, or F) and write RED on the relevant answer line to indicate the correct instructions for the Red route. Circle a different letter and write GREEN to indicate the Green route.

A Forward 3, Turn Right 90°, Forward 4, Turn Left 90°, Forward 6,
Turn Right 90°, Forward 4, Turn Left 90°, Forward 2. _____

B Forward 2, Turn Left 90°, Forward 5, Turn Right 90°, Forward 4,
Turn Left 90°, Forward 4, Turn Left 90°, Forward 2. _____

C Forward 2, Turn Left 90°, Forward 5, Turn Right 90°, Forward 5,
Turn Left 90°, Forward 1, Turn Right 90°, Forward 4. _____

D Forward 3, Turn Right 90°, Forward 3, Turn Left 90°, Forward 4,
Turn Left 90°, Forward 5, Turn Right 90°, Forward 6. _____

E Forward 3, Turn Right 90°, Forward 1, Turn Left 90°, Forward 3,
Turn Left 90°, Forward 4, Turn Right 90°, Forward 5. _____

F Forward 3, Turn Right 90°, Forward 1, Turn Right 90°, Forward 3,
Turn Left 90°, Forward 4, Turn Right 90°, Forward 5. _____

( ) 2

When I roll a fair dice what is the probability (expressed in **lowest term** fraction) that I will get:

**13** an odd number? _____     **14** a six? _____     **15** a 2 or a 4? _____

( ) 3

**16** Calculate the area of a square with a perimeter of 20 cm.     _____ cm²

( ) 1

**17–18** Circle the letters to indicate which of these nets would fold to make a closed cube.

( ) 2

5

A `22:17`  B `13:05`  C `14:22`

**19–21** What times will these digital clocks show in $3\frac{1}{4}$ hours time?

A ___ : ___　　　　B ___ : ___　　　　C ___ : ___

A `16:10`  B `17:27`  C `02:00`

**22–24** What times did these digital clocks show $2\frac{3}{4}$ hours ago?

A ___ : ___　　　　B ___ : ___　　　　C ___ : ___

**25–28** Write these fractions as decimals.

$7\frac{1}{2}$　　　　$9\frac{1}{20}$　　　　$6\frac{4}{40}$　　　　$8\frac{9}{50}$

_____　　_____　　_____　　_____

Put the appropriate signs in these calculations to make them correct.

**29** 63 ___ 6 = 10.5　　　　**30** 63 ___ 6 = 69　　　　**31** 63 ___ 6 = 57

A　　　　　　B　　　　　　C　　　　　　D

   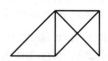

**32** A milk delivery woman goes along each street on her route only once. She doesn't mind if she passes over the same corner more than once. Which of the following routes is the one she *does not* take?

Rashid has a CD collection which he has sorted into three categories: Classical, Rock and Pop. He has four times as many Pop as Classical, and three times as many Rock as Classical. Altogether Rashid has 80 CDs.

**33** How many Classical CDs does he have?　　　　_____

**34** How many Rock CDs does he have?　　　　_____

**35** How many Pop CDs does he have?　　　　_____

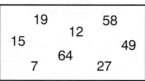

```
   19        58
       12
15            49
    64
   7     27
```

**36–39** Put circles around the **prime numbers** and squares around the square numbers.

What is the **median** in each of these sets of numbers?

B 15

  **40**  15    17    21    14    19    22    16 _____

  **41**  27    103    48    59    101    77    85 _____ **2**

What is the **mode** in each of these sets of numbers?

B 15

  **42**  36    40    41    36    35    40    36 _____

  **43**  0.8    0.75    0.5    0.4    0.5    0.1    0.8    0.5 _____ **2**

What is the **mean** in each of these sets of numbers?

B 15

  **44**  1.5    2.5    7.5    5.0    3.5 _____

  **45**  110    106    112    120    124    118 _____ **2**

B 14

Use this line graph, which is a conversion graph from miles to kilometres and from kilometres to miles, to answer these questions.

  **46**  What is 50 miles in kilometres? _____ km

  **47**  What is 120 kilometres in miles? _____ miles

  **48**  Approximately how many miles is 70 kilometres? _____ miles

  **49**  Approximately how many kilometres is 60 miles? _____ km

  **50**  Which is the greater, 25 miles or 35 kilometres? _____ **5**

# Paper 3

I made this large rectangle from four smaller ones.

1 What is the area of rectangle A? _____

2 What is the area of rectangle B? _____

3 What is the area of rectangle C? _____

4 What is the area of rectangle D? _____

5 What is the perimeter of the large rectangle? _____

6–11 A local computer shop is putting up its prices. Everything will go up by $12\frac{1}{2}\%$. Complete this table.

| Price | Price rise | Total price |
|-------|-----------|-------------|
| £20 | £_____ | £_____ |
| £50 | £_____ | £_____ |
| £100 | £_____ | £_____ |

12 Orla's angelfish had a **mean** number of 9 babies each. There are 72 baby angelfish in her tank. How many mother angelfish does she have? _____

What number does each symbol represent?

13 $\blacktriangle \times 7 = (2 \times 6) + (2 \times 8)$    $\blacktriangle$ = _____

14 $12 + 15 = 3 \times \bullet$    $\bullet$ = _____

15 $4 \times 11 = (2 \times 2) + (8 \times \blacksquare)$    $\blacksquare$ = _____

Jerzy put 54 strawberries into small, medium and large bowls in the ratio $1 : 2 : 3$. How many are in:

16 the small bowl? _____

17 the medium bowl? _____

18 the large bowl? _____

**19–20** What is $4^2$? _____

What **prime number** is closest to this? _____

**21–22** What is $6^2$? _____

What **prime number** is closest to this? _____

Calculate the area of these triangles.
Scale: each square represents 1 cm².

**23** _____   **24** _____   **25** _____   **26** _____

Write these to the nearest 10.

**27** 583 _____   **28** 737 _____

Write these to the nearest 100.

**29** 1549 _____   **30** 2378 _____

Write these to the nearest 1000.

**31** 23 501 _____   **32** 79 605 _____

18 minutes

Craggytown
(10 minutes at the quay)

Bluestrands
Bay

Sandyville
(10 minutes at the quay)

14 minutes

**33–37** A ferry crosses Bluestrands Bay from Craggytown to Sandyville and back again all day. Here is a part of the ferry timetable for one morning when the tide makes the journey from Sandyville to Craggytown quicker than the other way. Fill in the missing sailing times.

| Leave Craggytown | Leave Sandyville |
| --- | --- |
| 9:00 a.m. | _____ a.m. |
| _____ a.m. | _____ a.m. |
| _____ a.m. | _____ a.m. |

Give the answer to each calculation using the combined forms of measurement shown.

**38** 589 cm + 392 cm = _____ m _____ cm

**39** 607 cm − 209 cm = _____ m _____ cm

**40** 770 cm × 5 = _____ m _____ cm

**41** 1506 g + 2344 g = _____ kg _____ g

**42** 4380 g − 1820 g = _____ kg _____ g

Here are some prices in a local shop.

Bottle of fabric softener      £1.69
Pack of scouring pads      £1.99
Packet of soap powder      £2.49
Bottle of washing-up liquid      £1.58

**43–44** Wasim bought two of these items and got 52p change from a £5.00 note.
Which two did Wasim buy? _____ and _____

**45** What would be the cost of five packs of scouring pads? £ _____

**46** Melanie bought a bottle of fabric softener, a pack of scouring pads and a bottle of washing-up liquid. What change was she given from a £20 note? £ _____

**47–50** In a nearby shop there was a sale in which everything was being sold at a third off. Complete this table to show the original, full price.

| Sale price | Original, full price |
|---|---|
| £6.46 | _____ |
| £10.86 | _____ |
| £12.50 | _____ |
| £58.24 | _____ |

*Now go to the Progress Chart to record your score!*     Total   50

# Paper 4

You spin this hexagonal spinner with coloured segments. Circle the correct probability for these spins.

**1** What is the probability of spinning red?

$\frac{1}{3}$      $\frac{2}{3}$      $\frac{1}{2}$      $\frac{1}{6}$

**2** What is the probability of spinning green?

$\frac{1}{2}$      $\frac{1}{5}$      $\frac{1}{6}$      $\frac{2}{5}$

**3** What is the probability of spinning purple, orange or yellow?

$\frac{1}{6}$ $\qquad$ $\frac{1}{2}$ $\qquad$ $\frac{5}{6}$ $\qquad$ $\frac{2}{3}$

**4** What is the probability of spinning blue or purple?

$\frac{2}{3}$ $\qquad$ $\frac{1}{3}$ $\qquad$ $\frac{5}{6}$ $\qquad$ $\frac{2}{5}$

Which numbers are the arrows pointing to on this number line?

**5** Arrow A

**6** Arrow B

**7** Arrow C

**8** Arrow D

What number does each letter represent?

**9** $4 \times a = 14 - 2$ $\qquad\qquad\qquad\qquad$ $a = $ _____

**10** $(5 \times b) - (2 \times b) = 15$ $\qquad\qquad$ $b = $ _____

**11** $(3 \times c) + c = 12$ $\qquad\qquad\quad$ $c = $ _____

**12** $(4 \times d) + (3 \times d) = 28$ $\qquad\quad$ $d = $ _____

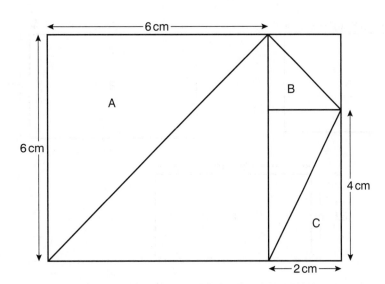

I made this large rectangle from six triangles.
Write in the area of:

**13** triangle A _____ $\qquad$ **14** triangle B _____

**15** triangle C _____ $\qquad$ **16** the large rectangle _____

11

**17–19** Some digits are missing in these calculations. Write them in.

    5 __ __ 5
   __  9  2  7
+   2  6  4 __
─────────────
  1  1  7  4  3
```

```
  1 __ 8 __
− 8 __ 9
──────────
  8  2  4
```

```
      4  5  6
×        __ __
──────────────
   2  2  8  0
```

**20** What is the perimeter of this shape? _____

**21** What is the area of this shape? _____

Divide each of these by 100.

**22** 1.65 _____   **23** 0.483 _____

**24** 0.3217 _____   **25** 0.0791 _____

Calculate the area and the perimeter of each of these rectangles.

**26–27** A:   Area = _____ cm²   Perimeter = _____ cm

**28–29** B:   Area = _____ cm²   Perimeter = _____ cm

**30–31** C:   Area = _____ cm²   Perimeter = _____ cm

B 2
B 3
3
B 20
2
B 1
4
B 20
6
```

Here are some mathematics test results.

15    26    30    40    26    17    43    34    28    44    38    19

**32** What is the **range**? _____

**33** What is the **median**? _____

**34** What is the **mode**? _____

**35** What is the **mean**? _____

Underline the correct answer to each of these calculations.

**36** $0.25 \times 0.25 =$    62.5    6.25    0.625    0.0625    0.006 25

**37** $736 \div 200 =$    8.36    3.68    3.86    6.83    6.38

**38** $0.316 \div 0.4 =$    0.0079    0.079    79    0.79    7.9

Complete these calculations.

**39**
$$36\overline{)1332}$$

**40**
$$24\overline{)1152}$$

**41**
$$39\overline{)1053}$$

Divide these numbers by 10.

**42** 21.73    _____

**43** 5.46    _____

**44** 0.189    _____

A  `15:26`    B  `08:30`    C  `21:18`

**45–50** What will the time be in $1\frac{3}{4}$ hours? Write the answer first for a 24-hour clock, then for a 12-hour clock.

A  __ : __   or   _____

B  __ : __   or   _____

C  __ : __   or   _____

# Paper 5

In a survey, 300 families were asked where in Europe they went on holiday last year. Here are their replies in percentages.

| Austria | 6% | Belgium | 4% |
|---|---|---|---|
| France | 23% | Germany | 3% |
| Greece | 10% | Ireland | 4% |
| Italy | 6% | Netherlands | 3% |
| Spain | 35% | Switzerland | 4% |
| Other countries | 2% | | |

1 How many people went to France? _____

2 Which was the most popular destination? _____

3 How many families went to Austria or Switzerland? _____

4 How many families went to Germany or Belgium? _____

5 How many fewer families went to Greece than to Spain? _____

I went shopping yesterday. It took me 15 minutes to walk to the first shop where I stayed for 38 minutes. Three minutes later I entered another shop and stayed there for 27 minutes. Then I walked home taking 21 minutes to do so. I left home at 9:30 a.m.

6 What time did I get back home? _____ a.m.

7 What time did I enter the second shop? _____ a.m.

Complete these sequences.

8–9    256    128    64    32    _____ _____

10–11   53     49     45    41    _____ _____

12–13   7      14     28    56    _____ _____

14–18 A bike shop increased its prices by 10%. Complete the table.

| Old price | New price |
|---|---|
| £60 | £ _____ |
| £200 | £ _____ |
| £340 | £ _____ |
| £255 | £ _____ |
| £405 | £ _____ |

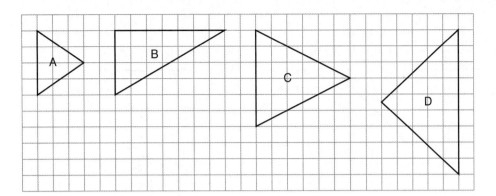

Find the area of these triangles.
Scale: each square represents 1 cm².

B 18

**19–22** A _____     B _____     C _____     D _____

4

B 20

Now find the area of these shapes.
Scale: each square represents 1 cm².

**23–26** A _____     B _____     C _____     D _____

4

B 3
B 13

| British pounds | US dollars | Euros | Indian rupees | Philippine pesos |
|----------------|------------|-------|---------------|------------------|
| £1 | 1.87 | 1.46 | 87 | 96 |

**27** How many Euros do you get for £50?     € _____

**28** How many Indian rupees do you get for £50?     _____ rupees

**29** How many British pounds do you get for 374 US dollars?     £ _____

**30** How many Philippine pesos do you get for £200?     _____ pesos

4

B 3

**31** An article costs £6.75. How much would 6 of these articles cost?     £ _____

1

Circle TRUE or FALSE for each of these statements.

**32** Line C is parallel to Line H.          TRUE          FALSE

**33** Line G is vertical.          TRUE          FALSE

**34** Line B is horizontal.          TRUE          FALSE

**35** Line D is parallel to Line H.          TRUE          FALSE

**36** Line E is perpendicular to Line H.          TRUE          FALSE

**37** Line A is perpendicular to Line F.          TRUE          FALSE

**38–41** Draw a circle around the **prime numbers** in this box.

Turn the following lengths into kilometres.

**42** 1897 m =          _____ km

**43** 23 873 m =          _____ km

**44** 632 m =          _____ km

**45** Annushka rides her horse at a steady canter and covers 5 metres every second.
If it takes them 80 seconds to canter around the edge of the home
paddock, what is the perimeter of the paddock?          _____ m

**46** The **mean** of the following ten numbers is 2.4. Find the missing number.

2    6    1    2    3    2    1    4    1    _____

16

A swimming pool contains 4 million litres of water.

**47** When it is $\frac{1}{5}$ full how many litres are in it? _____ litres

**48** What % of the content is 600 000 litres? _____%

**49** For cleaning it is filled with only $\frac{1}{50}$ of its entire contents. How much water is this? _____ litres

**50** If the pool has eight lanes, how much water is in each lane? _____ litres

*Now go to the Progress Chart to record your score!* **Total** 50

# Paper 6

Here are some of the highest mountains in the UK. Write the height of each to the nearest 100 feet.

| | | | |
|---|---|---|---|
| **1** | Ben Nevis, Scotland | 4408 feet | _____ feet |
| **2** | Ben Macdhui, Scotland | 4296 feet | _____ feet |
| **3** | Ben Lawers, Scotland | 3984 feet | _____ feet |
| **4** | Snowdon, Wales | 3560 feet | _____ feet |
| **5** | Scafell Pike, England | 3206 feet | _____ feet |
| **6** | Slieve Donard, N. Ireland | 2796 feet | _____ feet |

Put the correct sign $<$, $>$ or $=$ in these calculations.

**7** $7 \times 8$ ___ $5 \times 11$

**8** $11 + 9 + 10$ ___ $29 + 2$

**9** $6^2$ ___ $4 \times 9$

**10** $0.75\,m$ ___ $760\,cm$

**11** $105\,min$ ___ $1\frac{3}{4}$ hour

**12** $5 \times 10$ ___ $7^2$

**13–15** Write down the numbers that will come out of this machine.

17

A bag contains 5 grey balls, 4 white balls and 1 black ball. Underline the correct answer to each question.

B 16

**16** What is the probability of picking a grey ball?

$\frac{4}{5}$      $\frac{1}{2}$      $\frac{3}{5}$      $\frac{1}{5}$      $\frac{1}{10}$

**17** What is the probability of picking a black ball?

$\frac{1}{100}$      $\frac{1}{10}$      $\frac{1}{5}$      $\frac{4}{5}$

**18** What is the probability of picking a white ball?

$\frac{1}{5}$      $\frac{2}{5}$      $\frac{3}{5}$      $\frac{4}{5}$      $\frac{9}{10}$

**19** What is the probability of picking a ball that is not grey, white or black?

$\frac{1}{10}$      $\frac{3}{5}$      $0$      $\frac{1}{2}$

**20–23** Calculate these angles.

A = _____ °      B = _____ °      C = _____ °      D = _____ °

B 17
B 18
B 3
B 25

**24–27** In the chiller cabinet in my local shop there are supplies of fresh cream and milk. If the following supplies were in the cabinet on two different days, how much cream and milk was there?

Day 1:   6 pots of cream = _____ ml          8 cartons of milk = \_\_\_ l _____ ml

Day 2:  14 pots of cream = \_\_\_ l _____ ml          11 cartons of milk = \_\_\_ l _____ ml

Solve these calculations.

B2/B3

**28**    6839
    + 2165
_____

**29** $(9 \times 8) + 25 =$ _____

**30** $(275 \div 22) + 7 =$ _____

**31**
    _____
16⟌304

**32**
    _____
28⟌896

**33** $9.3 - 5.4 =$ _____    **6**

Insert the missing signs to make these statements correct.    B2/B3

**34–35** $(6 \_\_ 4) \_\_ 5 = 2$

**36–37** $6 \_\_ 3 \_\_ 2 = 9$

**38–39** $5 \_\_ 4 \_\_ 2 = 7$    **6**

Turn the following lengths into metres.    B  25

**40** 365 cm = _____    **41** 15 678 cm = _____    **2**

B  20

2x

x

**42** What is the area of this shape? _____    **1**

**43–45** What are the **prime factors** of 42? _____, _____ and _____    B5/B6

**3**

Calculate these percentages.    B  12

**46** 15% of 240 = _____

**47** 25% of 112 = _____

**48** 30% of 1860 = _____

**49** 75% of 96 = _____

**50** 15% of 300 = _____    **5**

# Paper 7

1 Last year, in months with 31 days, I collected *m* tokens.
   In months with 30 days I collected *2m* tokens.
   For the rest of the year I collected *3m* tokens.
   How many tokens did I collect last year? _____

Round these numbers to the nearest 1000.

2 63 501 _____

3 128 609 _____

| British pounds | Euros | NZ dollars | Thailand baht |
|:---:|:---:|:---:|:---:|
| 1 | 1.5 | 3 | 70 |

How much would these items be in British pounds?

4 A pair of trainers costing 42 Euros. £ _____

5 A packet of biscuits costing 6 NZ dollars. £ _____

6 A cake costing 245 baht. £ _____

Write these **mixed numbers** in their **lowest terms**.

7 $4\frac{12}{18}$ _____

8 $6\frac{25}{75}$ _____

9 $3\frac{14}{21}$ _____

Write these decimals as fractions in their **lowest terms**.

10 2.6 _____

11 10.4 _____

12 3.05 _____

13 7.75 _____

Find the answers to these calculations.

14 $6.5 + 3.05 =$ _____

15 $4 \times 1.25 =$ _____

16 $3.75 - 2.95 =$ _____

17 $9 \div 0.3 =$ _____

**18** Three roadside flashing beacons are all switched on at the same time. One flashes every 6 seconds, one every 9 seconds and the third every 12 seconds. How many seconds after being switched on do they flash at the same time?

_____ seconds

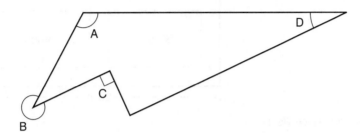

**19–22** Use **acute**, **obtuse**, right-angled or **reflex** to describe the angles marked A–D.

A _____  B _____  C _____  D _____

Jack is a window cleaner. He carries three ladders. The shortest ladder is half as long as the middle ladder. The longest ladder is twice as long as the middle ladder. If he joins all of the ladders together he can climb 42 feet.

**23–25** How long is each ladder?

Shortest _____ feet

Middle _____ feet

Longest _____ feet

Fifteen children sat a science test. Here are their results:

| 30 | 32 | 28 | 29 | 30 | 28 | 30 | 26 |
| 27 | 28 | 26 | 27 | 26 | 30 | 30 |

**26** What is the **mode**?  _____

**27** What is the **range**?  _____

**28** What is the **median**?  _____

**29** The total marks obtained in a mathematics test were 384. If the **mean** was 24, how many children took the test?  _____

Find the answers to these calculations.

**30** $6.3\,m + 12.8\,m + 73.5\,m =$ _____ m

**31** $160\,ml + 820\,ml + 0.5\,l =$ _____ l

**32** $803\,g + 1.6\,kg + 326\,g =$ _____ kg

This is the plan of a formal garden.
All of the paths are 2 m wide.
The rose beds are square, and the shrub beds are rectangles of equal size.

 B 20

**33** What is the area of a rose bed? _____

**34** What is the area of a shrub bed? _____

**35** What is the perimeter of a rose bed? _____

**36** What is the perimeter of a shrub bed? _____

 4

 B 6

**37** What is $9^2$? _____

**38** What is 49 written as a square number? _____

 2

 B 23

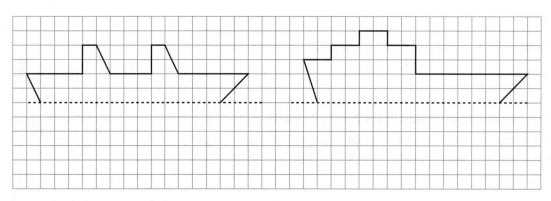

**39–40** Draw in the reflections of these two ships.

 2

**41–44** Karla manages four salespeople. She decides to give each of them a 7.5% rise in salary. What are their new salaries?

B 12

| Name | Salary | New salary |
|---|---|---|
| Mrs Jones | £21 000 | £ _____ |
| Mr Yusef | £18 000 | £ _____ |
| Ms Samson | £19 000 | £ _____ |
| Mr Smith | £20 500 | £ _____ |

 4

TV1 and TV2 are television channels both showing films that start at 8:30 p.m.
TV1 puts on advertisements every 10 minutes after the start of a film.
TV2 puts on advertisements every 15 minutes after the start of a film.

**45** What is the earliest time that there will be advertisements on both
channels at the same time? _____ p.m.

**46** If the shortest film ends after 2 hours, how many times (during the films) will
advertisements appear on both channels at the same time? _____

Here is a list of some of the largest lakes in the world. Write the area of each lake to the
nearest 1000 km².

**47** Lake Victoria    62 940 km²    _____

**48** Lake Huron    59 580 km²    _____

**49** Lake Michigan    57 700 km²    _____

**50** Lake Baikal    31 494 km²    _____

*Now go to the Progress Chart to record your score!*    Total    50

# Paper 8

**1** One cross-stitch picture needs 529 cross stitches to make it. How many
cross stitches are there in 13 pictures? _____

**2** A garden wall needs 35 rows of 228 bricks. How many bricks is this? _____

**3** The library van delivers 1014 books to a school for 13 groups of children.
How many books are there for each group? _____

**4** There are 11 players in a football team. There are enough children in a
school to make 17 football teams with 2 substitutes for each team.
How many children are there in the school? _____

**5** Which of the following shapes has a perimeter of 10 cm? Circle the answer.

A   a square with sides of 2 cm

B   a rectangle with sides of 2 cm and 4 cm

C   a regular pentagon with sides of 2 cm

D   a regular hexagon with sides of 2 cm

If $x = 3$ and $y = 4$, find the value of these equations.

**6** $4y - 3x =$ _____

**7** $9x + 9y =$ _____

**8** $7x - 3y =$ _____

**9** $2x \times y =$ _____

FLATCARE manages a block of flats. It costs between £75 and £220 per week to rent a flat. FLATCARE charges 3% of the rent for their services.

Complete this table.

| Rent for the flat | FLATCARE charges | |
|---|---|---|
| 1 week | 4 weeks | 52 weeks |
| £75 | _____ | _____ |
| £150 | _____ | _____ |
| £180 | _____ | _____ |
| £220 | _____ | _____ |

What are the **prime factors** of:

**18–20** 105?  _____, _____ and _____

**21–23** 231?  _____, _____ and _____

**24–26** Shape A has _____ faces, _____ edges and _____ **vertices**.

**27–29** Shape B has _____ faces, _____ edges and _____ **vertices**.

Round these numbers to the nearest 100.

**30** 21 512  _____

**31** 48 167  _____

**32** 113 851  _____

**33** Which is more: 1 lb or 1 kg of chickpeas?  _____

**34** Which is less: 60 g or $1\frac{1}{2}$ oz of cannellini beans?  _____

**35** Which is more: 500 g or 12 oz of lentils?  _____

**36** Which is less: 10.5 lb or 1.05 kg of red kidney beans?  _____

**37** To make up a pack of 2.5 kg of dried apricots, how many grams have to be added to 1.03 kg? _____ g

**38** There are 37 packs of raisins. Each pack weighs 45 g. How much do all of the packs weigh altogether? _____ kg

Here are the timetables of two trains on the Transpennine railway.

|  | Train 1 | Train 2 |
|---|---|---|
| Cleethorpes | 07:15 | 16:55 |
| Grimsby Town | 07:23 | 16:46 |
| Habrough | 07:33 | 16:31 |
| Barnetby | 07:41 | 16:22 |
| Scunthorpe | 07:56 | 16:08 |
| Doncaster | 08:25 depart 08:27 | 15:40 depart 15:42 |
| Meadowhall | 08:46 | 15:17 |
| Sheffield | 08:54 depart 09:10 | 15:08 depart 15:11 |
| Stockport | 09:51 | 13:40 |
| Manchester Piccadilly | 10:04 | 14:19 |
| Manchester Airport | 10:31 | 13:56 |

**39** How long does Train 1 take to travel from Cleethorpes to Manchester Airport?

_____

**40** How long does Train 2 take to travel from Manchester Airport to Cleethorpes?

_____

Write in hours and / or minutes how long the following journeys take.

**41** Habrough to Meadowhall _____

**42** Sheffield to Manchester Piccadilly _____

**43** Doncaster to Barnetby _____

**44** Sheffield to Grimsby Town _____

In a bag of marbles there are 8 cat's eyes for every 5 pearlies. Altogether there are 247 marbles.

**45** How many cat's eyes are there? _____

**46** How many pearlies are there? _____

Fill in the missing number in each of these calculations.

**47** $12 \times 11 \times$ _____ $= 1188$

**48** _____ $\times 9 \times 15 = 945$

**49** $13 \times 8 \div$ _____ $= 26$

**50** $(7 \times 8) \times ($ _____ $+ 4) = 840$

*Now go to the Progress Chart to record your score!* **Total** 50

25

# Paper 9

| 1 | 6817 − 948 | 2 | 7008 − 4109 | 3 | 16 835 − 8748 | 4 | 23 642 − 15 863 |
|---|---|---|---|---|---|---|---|

Complete these sequences.

**5–6** 0.125    0.2    0.275   _____  _____

**7–8** $8\frac{1}{2}$    $7\frac{3}{4}$    7   _____  _____

**9–10** 9.5    12.5    16.5    21.5   _____  _____

**11–13** What is the missing number in each of these number squares?

| 83 | 76 | 69 |
|---|---|---|
| 90 | A | 76 |
| 97 | 90 | 83 |

A = _____

| 117 | 124 | 131 |
|---|---|---|
| 110 | 117 | 124 |
| B | 110 | 117 |

B = _____

| 78 | 90 | C |
|---|---|---|
| 66 | 78 | 90 |
| 54 | 66 | 78 |

C = _____

What is $\frac{1}{100}$ of each of these values?

**14** 2342     _____

**15** 66.75     _____

**16** 10.04     _____

**17** 3.675     _____

**18–21** What are the **factors** of 18?

    1, _____, _____, _____, _____ and 18

Kitchen scales     Oven pot     Cooking tool set     Can opener

£8.50     £3.20     £7.99     £4.75

B 3
B 2

Mrs Perhar is restocking her cooking shop. She buys some of the items shown here. What does she spend on these items?

**22** 5 kitchen scales       £ _____

**23** 8 oven pots       £ _____

**24** 10 cooking tool sets       £ _____

**25** 12 can openers       £ _____

**26** How much does Mrs Perhar spend altogether?       £ _____

5

**27–32** Match the names of these polygons to the shapes by drawing lines between them.

B 18
B 19

**Trapezium**

**Kite**

Equilateral triangle

**Rhombus**

**Parallelogram**

Pentagon

6

Find the value of x, y and z in these equations.

B8/B3
B2/B6

**33** $2y \div 3 = 4$       $y =$ _____

**34** $3x + 36 = 45$       $x =$ _____

**35** $z^2 = 49$       $z =$ _____

Now use the values that you have found for x, y and z to solve these equations.

B8/B2
B 4

**36** $4x + 5y + 3z =$       _____

**37** $2x^2 + 3y - z =$       _____

5

**38** A ride on the Fear Generator costs £$t$ and a ride on the Gut Wrencher costs £$s$.
Expressed as an equation, what did Lou spend if he had 6 rides
on the Gut Wrencher and 3 rides on the Fear Generator? _____

B 8
1

B 14

**39** What was the temperature on Saturday? _____ °C

**40** What was the temperature on Thursday? _____ °C

**41** What is the difference between the highest and lowest temperatures in
the week? _____ °

3

**42–47** Complete this table:

B 20

| Perimeter of rectangle | Length = 4 × width | Width |
|---|---|---|
| 30 cm | _____ cm | _____ cm |
| 50 cm | _____ cm | _____ cm |
| 80 cm | _____ cm | _____ cm |

6

B1/B10

**48** Write twenty-six thousand, four hundred and four in numbers. _____

**49** Write 17 058 in words. _____

**50** Write one tenth of four hundred and sixteen in numbers. _____

3

*Now go to the Progress Chart to record your score!* **Total** 50

Find the sum of these weights.

**1** $275\,g + 1.5\,kg + 320\,g =$ _____ kg

**2** $806\,g + 2.3\,kg + 196\,g =$ _____ kg

Find the difference in these weights.

**3** $1.65\,kg$ and $860\,g =$ _____ kg

**4** $14.8\,kg$ and $2650\,g =$ _____ kg

Calculate these divisions, giving the answers in metres.

**5** $2.2\,km \div 8 =$ _____ m

**6** $1.33\,km \div 7 =$ _____ m

What are the **coordinates** of:

**7** Shaleton?

( _____ , _____ )

**8** Sandy Bay?

( _____ , _____ )

**9** Netherton?

( _____ , _____ )

What place is located:

**10** NE of Speckle Hill?

_____

**11** due west of Fresh Harbour?

_____

**12** SW of Netherton?

_____

B 25
B 2
2

B 25
B 2
2

B 25
B 3
2

B 23

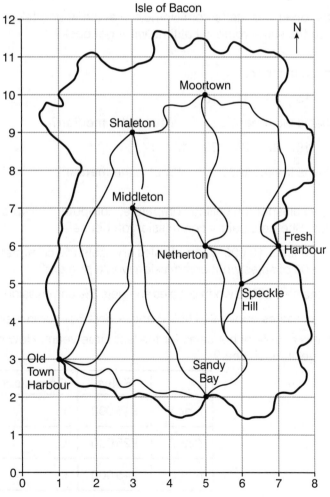

Isle of Bacon

6

There are two buses on the Isle of Bacon. Here is the morning timetable for one of the buses:

| Netherton (out) | 09:00 |
| Sandy Bay | 09:15 |
| Old Town Harbour | 09:35 |
| Middleton | 10:00 |
| Shaleton | 10:15 |
| Moortown | 10:23 |
| Fresh Harbour | 10:50 |
| Speckle Hill | 11:02 |
| Netherton (return) | 11:18 |

**13** How long does it take to travel from Netherton to Old Town Harbour? _____ minutes

**14** How long does it take to travel from Old Town Harbour back
to Netherton?                                                _____ h _____ min

**15** How long does it take to travel from Moortown back to Netherton?  _____ minutes

**16** If the other bus starts from Netherton at 09:30 and takes the same time
to do the same route, what time will it get back?                    ___ : ___         4

Look at these numbers.

**17–19** 10   15   20   12   18

What is the **mean**? ___      What is the **median**? ___      What is the **range**? ___

**20–22** 14   19   27   24   26   13   17

What is the **mean**? ___      What is the **median**? ___      What is the **range**? ___         6

Frances is a salesperson selling computers, computer software and computer
accessories. She gets paid a commission on her sales.

**23** On her first £10 000 worth of sales she gets 2% commission. If she makes
£10 000 of sales what commission would she get?                    £ _____

**24** On the next £5000 worth of sales she gets 3% commission. How much is that?  £ _____

**25–27** For any sales above £15 000 Frances gets 5% commission.

Here is a table of her sales for the last three years. How much commission does
she get in each year?

|        | **Sales** | **Commission** |
|--------|-----------|----------------|
| Year 1 | £15 000 | £ |
| Year 2 | £25 000 | £ |
| Year 3 | £45 000 | £ |

5

How many lines of symmetry do the following shapes have?

**28** An isosceles triangle ___     **29** A regular pentagon ___

**30** A **kite**     ___     **31** A square     ___

**32–34** Find-a-place Estate Agents charge a 2% fee on the selling price of a house. What fee did that they charge on these properties?

| Selling price | 2% fee |
|---|---|
| £175 000 | £ _____ |
| £235 000 | £ _____ |
| £380 000 | £ _____ |

Work out these values.

**35** one twelfth of 192 ___     **36** one twelfth of 540 ___

**37** one twelfth of 996 ___     **38** one twelfth of 1080 ___

**39–41** Mia spent a day out birdwatching and made a note of all the birds she saw. At the end of the day she noticed there were 4 starlings to 3 sparrows to 1 robin. If she counted 56 birds altogether, how many were:

starlings? ___     sparrows? ___     robins? ___

In a tropical aquarium there are 8 guppies for every 3 swordtails. There are 121 fish altogether. How many are:

**42** guppies?     ___

**43** swordtails?     ___

Round these numbers to the nearest 10.

**44** 13 126 _____     **45** 29 533 _____     **46** 106 044 _____

Find the answers to these calculations.

**47** $\frac{1}{6} + \frac{1}{3} =$ ___     **48** $\frac{3}{10} + \frac{3}{5} =$ ___

**49** $12 \times \frac{1}{3} =$ ___     **50** $1\frac{1}{2} + 1\frac{2}{10} =$ ___

*Now go to the Progress Chart to record your score!* Total 50

B 18
B 19
B 24
4
B 12
3
B 10
4
B 13
3
B 13
2
B 1
3
B10/B2
B 3
4

## Paper 11

The diagram consists of a larger square with a smaller square drawn at its centre.

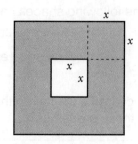

B 20

**1** What is the area of the shaded part of this shape? _____ ○ 1

Multiply these by 100.

B 1

**2** 60.3 _____ **3** 7.51 _____ ○ 2

Multiply these by 1000.

B 1

**4** 6.03 _____ **5** 12.12 _____ **6** 0.635 _____ ○ 3

A sports outfitter sold 120 T-shirts last week. Here is a pie chart showing the percentage of different colours sold.

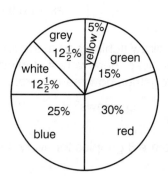

B 12
B 14
B 2

**7** How many grey T-shirts were sold? _____

**8** How many red T-shirts were sold? _____

**9** How many white and green T-shirts were sold altogether? _____

**10** How many more blue than yellow T-shirts were sold? _____ ○ 4

Put one number from column A and one number from column B into each of these statements to make them true.

| A | B |
|---|---|
| $\frac{4}{3}$ | 0.09 |
| 7.01 | $\frac{3}{50}$ |
| 10% | $\sqrt{36}$ |

**11–12** _____ < 7 < _____

**13–14** _____ < 0.7 < _____

**15–16** _____ < 0.07 < _____

A 6
B 10
B 11
B 12
B 6

○ 6

Any answer that requires units of measurement should be marked wrong if the correct units have not been included.

## Paper 1

1. 200 020
2. 49 049
3. 5
4. ÷
5. ÷
6. +
7. −
8. −
9. −
10. ×
11–14. $(^-6, ^-3)$, $(^-3, 4)$, $(3, 4)$, $(6, ^-3)$
15. Trapezium
16. 38
17. 46
18. $\frac{1}{3}$ of 8
19. $\frac{1}{6}$
20. $\frac{17}{40}$
21. $\frac{1}{4}$
22. 0.0507
23. $\frac{1}{4}$
24. $\frac{1}{8}$
25. 25%
26. 84
27. 36
28. 24
29. 6
30. 6
31. 7
32. 15
33. 18
34. 18
35. 147
36. 237
37. 357
38. 467
39. $5p + 2q$
40. 100.6
41. 2.65
42. 1.388
43. 4.0615
44. 60°
45. 150°
46. 30°
47. 120°
48. 5
49. 10
50. 25

## Paper 2

1. 1677
2. 3384
3. 221
4. 15 165
5. 5615
6. 1306
7. 10.7
8. 31.26

9. 4.585
10. 0.1173
11. C (Red)
12. E (Green)
13. $\frac{1}{2}$
14. $\frac{1}{6}$
15. $\frac{1}{3}$
16. 25
17. B
18. E
19. 01:32
20. 16:20
21. 17:37
22. 13:25
23. 14:42
24. 23:15
25. 7.5
26. 9.05
27. 6.1
28. 8.18
29. ÷
30. +
31. −
32. C
33. 10
34. 30
35. 40
36–39.

40. 17
41. 77
42. 36
43. 0.5
44. 4
45. 115
46. 80
47. 75
48. 44
49. 96
50. 25 miles

## Paper 3

1. 15 cm²
2. 12 cm²
3. 6 cm²
4. 12 cm²
5. 28 cm

6–11.

| Price | Price rise | Total price |
|-------|-----------|-------------|
| £20 | £2.50 | £22.50 |
| £50 | £6.25 | £56.25 |
| £100 | £12.50 | £112.50 |

12. 8
13. 4
14. 9
15. 5
16. 9
17. 18

18. 27
19. 16
20. 17
21. 36
22. 37
23. 5 cm²
24. $7\frac{1}{2}$ cm² or 7.5 cm²
25. 14 cm²
26. 12 cm²
27. 580
28. 740
29. 1500
30. 2400
31. 24 000
32. 80 000

33–37.

| Leave Craggytown | Leave Sandyville |
|------------------|------------------|
| **9:00** a.m. | **9:28** a.m. |
| **9:52** a.m. | **10:20** a.m. |
| **10:44** a.m. | **11:12** a.m. |

38. 9 m 81 cm
39. 3 m 98 cm
40. 38 m 5 cm
41. 3 kg 850 g
42. 2 kg 560 g
43–44. Soap powder, scouring pads
45. 9.95
46. 14.74
47. £9.69
48. £16.29
49. £18.75
50. £87.36

## Paper 4

1. $\frac{1}{6}$
2. $\frac{1}{6}$
3. $\frac{1}{2}$
4. $\frac{1}{3}$
5. 8.34
6. 8.38
7. 8.46
8. 8.52
9. 3
10. 5
11. 3
12. 4
13. 18 cm²
14. 2 cm²
15. 4 cm²
16. 48 cm²
17.
```
   5 1 7 5
   3 9 2 7
 +  2 6 4 1
  1 1 7 4 3
```
18.
```
  1 6 8 3
 −  8 5 9
    8 2 4
```

Bond Maths Assessment Papers 10-11+ years Book 2

**19**

$$\begin{array}{r} 4\,5\,6 \\ \times \quad 5 \\ \hline 2\,2\,8\,0 \end{array}$$

**20** 44 mm
**21** 70 mm$^2$
**22** 0.0165
**23** 0.00483
**24** 0.003217
**25** 0.000791
**26** 22
**27** 19
**28** 29.75
**29** 22.5
**30** 22.75
**31** 20
**32** 29
**33** 29
**34** 26
**35** 30
**36** 0.0625
**37** 3.68
**38** 0.79
**39** 37
**40** 48
**41** 27
**42** 2.173
**43** 0.546
**44** 0.0189
**45** 17:11
**46** 5:11 p.m.
**47** 10:15
**48** 10:15 a.m.
**49** 23:03
**50** 11:03 p.m.

## Paper 5

**1** 69
**2** Spain
**3** 30
**4** 21
**5** 75
**6** 11:14
**7** 10:26
**8** 16
**9** 8
**10** 37
**11** 33
**12** 112
**13** 224
**14** 66
**15** 220
**16** 374
**17** 280.50
**18** 445.50
**19** 6 cm$^2$
**20** 14 cm$^2$
**21** 18 cm$^2$
**22** 22.5 cm$^2$
**23** 12.5 cm$^2$
**24** 26 cm$^2$

**25** 28 cm$^2$
**26** 60 cm$^2$
**27** 73
**28** 4350
**29** 200
**30** 19 200
**31** 40.50
**32** FALSE
**33** FALSE
**34** TRUE
**35** TRUE
**36** TRUE
**37** FALSE

**38–41**

28    (37)    102
(19)  (5)  121
56    16    (29)    99

**42** 1.897
**43** 23.873
**44** 0.632
**45** 400
**46** 2
**47** 800 000
**48** 15%
**49** 80 000
**50** 500 000

## Paper 6

**1** 4400
**2** 4300
**3** 4000
**4** 3600
**5** 3200
**6** 2800
**7** >
**8** <
**9** =
**10** <
**11** =
**12** >
**13** 59
**14** 116
**15** 167
**16** $\frac{1}{2}$
**17** $\frac{1}{10}$
**18** $\frac{2}{5}$
**19** 0
**20** A = 120
**21** B = 60
**22** C = 40
**23** D = 58
**24** 852 ml
**25** 4 l 544 ml
**26** 1 l 988 ml
**27** 6 l 248 ml
**28** 9004
**29** 97
**30** 19.5

**31** 19
**32** 32
**33** 3.9
**34** +
**35** ÷
**36** ×
**37** ÷
**38** +
**39** −
**40** 3.65 m
**41** 156.78 m
**42** $2x^2$
**43–45** 2, 3, 7
**46** 36
**47** 28
**48** 558
**49** 72
**50** 45

## Paper 7

**1** 18 $m$
**2** 64 000
**3** 129 000
**4** 28
**5** 2
**6** 3.50
**7** $4\frac{2}{3}$
**8** $6\frac{1}{3}$
**9** $3\frac{2}{3}$
**10** $2\frac{3}{5}$
**11** $10\frac{2}{5}$
**12** $3\frac{1}{20}$
**13** $7\frac{3}{4}$
**14** 9.55
**15** 5
**16** 0.8
**17** 30
**18** 36
**19** Obtuse
**20** Reflex
**21** Right-angled
**22** Acute
**23** 6
**24** 12
**25** 24
**26** 30
**27** 6
**28** 28
**29** 16
**30** 92.6
**31** 1.48
**32** 2.729
**33** 36 m$^2$
**34** 60 m$^2$
**35** 24 m
**36** 32 m
**37** 81
**38** $7^2$

**39**

**40**

41 £22 575
42 £19 350
43 £20 425
44 £22 037.50
45 9:00
46 3
47 63 000 km²
48 60 000 km²
49 58 000 km²
50 31 000 km²

## Paper 8

1 6877
2 7980
3 78
4 221
5 C
6 7
7 63
8 9
9 24

**10–17**

| Rent for the flat | FLATCARE charges | |
|---|---|---|
| 1 week | 4 weeks | 52 weeks |
| £75 | £9 | £117 |
| £150 | £18 | £234 |
| £180 | £21.60 | £280.80 |
| £220 | £26.40 | £343.20 |

**18–20** 3, 5, 7
**21–23** 3, 7, 11
24 8
25 18
26 12
27 6
28 10
29 6
30 21 500
31 48 200
32 113 900
33 1 kg
34 1½ oz
35 500 g
36 1.05 kg

37 1470
38 1.665
39 3 h 16 min
40 2 h 59 min
41 1 h 13 min
42 54 min
43 40 min
44 1 h 35 min
45 152
46 95
47 9
48 7
49 4
50 11

## Paper 9

1 5869
2 2899
3 8087
4 7779
5 0.35
6 0.425
7 6¼
8 5½
9 27.5
10 34.5
11 83
12 103
13 102
14 23.42
15 0.6675
16 0.1004
17 0.03675
18 2
19 3
20 6
21 9
22 42.50
23 25.60
24 79.90
25 57.00
26 205.00

**27–32**

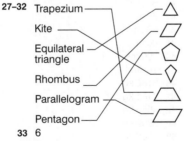

Trapezium
Kite
Equilateral triangle
Rhombus
Parallelogram
Pentagon

33 6
34 3
35 7
36 63
37 29
38 6s + 3t
39 6
40 ⁻2
41 10

**42–47**

| Perimeter | Length = 4 × width | Width |
|---|---|---|
| 30 cm | **12** cm | **3** cm |
| 50 cm | **20** cm | **5** cm |
| 80 cm | **32** cm | **8** cm |

48 26 404
49 Seventeen thousand and fifty-eight
50 41.6

## Paper 10

1 2.095
2 3.302
3 0.79
4 12.15
5 275
6 190
7 (3, 9)
8 (5, 2)
9 (5, 6)
10 Fresh Harbour
11 Netherton
12 Old Town Harbour
13 35
14 1 hr 43 minutes
15 55
16 11:48
17 15
18 15
19 10
20 20
21 19
22 14
23 200
24 150
25 350
26 850
27 1850
28 1
29 5
30 1
31 4
32 3500
33 4700
34 7600
35 16
36 45
37 83
38 90
39 28
40 21
41 7
42 88
43 33
44 13 130
45 29 530
46 106 040
47 ³⁄₆ or ½

48 $\frac{9}{10}$
49 4
50 $2\frac{7}{10}$

## Paper 11

1 $8x^2$
2 6030
3 751
4 6030
5 12120
6 635
7 15
8 36
9 33
10 24
11–12 $\sqrt{36} < 7 < 7.01$
13–14 $0.09 < 0.7 < \frac{4}{3}$
15–16 $\frac{3}{50} < 0.07 < 10\%$
17 60
18 120
19 360
20 3
21 0.5
22 11:30
23 12:00
24 74
25 69
26 1.04
27 129
28 17.83
29 541.86
30 1.50
31 46.8
32 47.15
33 47.6
34 47.95
35 48.05
36 3.87
37 4.58
38 6.47
39 4.77
40 19.69

41–44

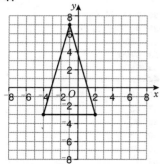

45 Isosceles triangle
46 (⁻1, 2)
47 192
48 1.5
49 1.44
50 10.1

## Paper 12

1 4
2 128 cm³
3 10
4 3
5 10
6 12
7 0.55
8 0.45
9 16°C
10 9:00 a.m.
11 23°C
12 10:30 a.m.
13 The children went out to play and left the door open.
14 28
15 6
16 28
17 27
18 180
19 30
20 25
21 5
22 10
23 64
24 34
25 36
26 $11^2$
27 8
28 16
29 24
30 $\frac{5}{10}$
31 $\frac{6}{12}$
32 $\frac{4}{12}$
33 $\frac{5}{15}$
34 $\frac{4}{20}$
35 $\frac{5}{25}$
36 73
37 101
38 63
39 100 m
40 600 m²
41 80 m
42 400 m²
43 60 m
44 200 m²
45 180 m
46 3180 kg
47 3161 kg
48 3555 kg
49 9896 kg
50 1060 kg

## Paper 13

1 97
2 0.097
3 400
4 4
5 6.75

6 0.675
7 11.5
8 0.115
9 19
10 0.019
11 3
12 13
13 21
14 42
15 17
16–21 Forward 3, Right 90°, Forward 2, Left 90°, Forward 4, Right 90°, Forward 2
22 166.50
23 0.65
24 27.45
25 26
26 8
27 27 cm²
28 47.05
29 0.22
30 12.55
31 42
32 56
33 14
34 5
35 8
36 9
37 10

38–40

41 80
42 18
43 24
44 10
45 10.07

| 46 | 23.75 |
| 47 | 28.50 |
| 48 | 15.47 |
| 49 | 1.70 |
| 50 | 9.01 |

## Paper 14

| 1 | 30° |
| 2 | 20° |
| 3 | 40° |
| 4 | 12:12 |
| 5 | 12:38 |
| 6 | 12:53 |
| 7 | 13:11 |
| 8 | 13:44 |
| 9 | 54.4 |
| 10 | 5.37 |
| 11 | 9.75 |
| 12 | 500 |
| 13 | 39p |
| 14 | 30p |
| 15 | 45p |
| 16 | 15 |
| 17 | 30 |
| 18 | 75 |
| 19 | 18 |
| 20 | 20 |
| 21 | 36 |
| 22 | 77 |
| 23 | 52 |
| 24 | 144 |

**25–31**

Three-circle Venn diagram: "Multiples of 3", "Multiples of 5", "Multiples of 7". 9 (only 3), 15 (3∩5), 10 (only 5), 105 (centre), 21 (3∩7), 35 (5∩7), 14 (only 7).

| 32 | $p - 8$ |
| 33 | 276.19 |
| 34 | $1832\frac{3}{5}$ |
| 35 | 4.5 |
| 36 | 38 915 |
| 37 | 33.02 |
| 38 | 60.80 |
| 39 | 1.70 |
| 40 | 42.90 |
| 41 | 3 |
| 42 | 4 |
| 43 | 6 |
| 44 | 60 |
| 45 | 167 |
| 46 | 122 |
| 47 | 59 |
| 48 | 100 |
| 49 | 5 |
| 50 | 20 |

Answers are correct to within 2° of these

## Paper 15

| 1 | 179 |
| 2 | 3.87 |
| 3 | 77 |
| 4 | 10.15 |
| 5 | 714 |
| 6 | 679 |
| 7 | 16 |
| 8 | 18 |
| 9 | 13.00 |
| 10 | 13.25 |
| 11 | $\frac{1}{32}$ |
| 12 | $\frac{1}{64}$ |
| 13 | 26 |
| 14 | 31 |

**15–20**

|  | Length | Width | Perimeter | Area |
|---|---|---|---|---|
| Rectangle 1 | 6 cm | 4 cm | **20** cm | **24** cm² |
| Rectangle 2 | 9 cm | **3** cm | 24 cm | **27** cm² |
| Rectangle 3 | **11** cm | 6 cm | **34** cm | 66 cm² |

| 21 | 10 |
| 22 | 75 |
| 23 | 50 |
| 24 | 250 |
| 25 | 8 |
| 26 | 19 |
| 27 | 6 |
| 28 | 110 |
| 29 | 9 |
| 30 | 34 |
| 31 | $20y^2$ |
| 32 | 40% |
| 33 | 15% |
| 34 | $\frac{1}{5}$ |
| 35 | $\frac{1}{4}$ |
| 36 | 16 |
| 37–38 | 17, 31 |
| 39 | Iris Parker |
| 40 | Sandy Young |
| 41 | Bob and Sally Macintosh |
| 42 | (7, 4) |
| 43 | (2, 2) |
| 44 | Bob and Sally Macintosh |
| 45 | 20 |
| 46 | 30 |
| 47 | 60 |
| 48–50 | B, D, F |

## Paper 16

| 1 | 2 |
| 2 | 3 |
| 3 | 5 |
| 4 | 2 |
| 5 | 5 |

| 6 | 11 |
| 7 | 3 |
| 8 | 5 |
| 9 | 11 |
| 10 | 8x |
| 11 | 53 |
| 12 | $\frac{7}{21}$ |
| 13 | 20% |
| 14 | 1.9 |
| 15 | 27 |
| 16 | 3.5 |
| 17 | 10.1 |
| 18 | 0.659 |
| 19 | 0.038 |
| 20 | 0.00165 |
| 21 | 4 |
| 22 | 2 |
| 23 | $\frac{1}{2}$ |
| 24 | $\frac{1}{4}$ |
| 25 | $1\frac{1}{3}$ |
| 26 | 1 |
| 27 | 12 |
| 28 | 3 |
| 29 | 21 |
| 30 | 12 |
| 31 | 38 |
| 32 | 13 |
| 33 | 28 |
| 34 | 6 |
| 35 | 3.12 |
| 36 | 7.45 |
| 37 | 4.94 |
| 38 | 33p |
| 39 | 58 |
| 40 | 24 |
| 41 | 20 |
| 42 | 54 |
| 43–46 | 78%, $\frac{2}{3}$, $\frac{17}{50}$, 23% |
| 47 | Square-based pyramid |
| 48 | Cuboid |
| 49 | Tetrahedron |
| 50 | Open-topped cube |

## Paper 17

| 1 | 22.8 |
| 2 | 64.68 |
| 3 | 60.8 |
| 4 | 42.55 |
| 5 | 34 |
| 6 | 190 |
| 7 | 3.2 |
| 8 | 23 |
| 9 | < |
| 10 | = |
| 11 | > |
| 12 | = |
| 13 | < |
| 14 | 50 |
| 15 | 75 |
| 16 | 150 |

17  30
18  400
19  60
20  6
21  8
22  3
23  48
24  28
25  18
26  18
27  24
28  22
29  One hundred and seventy-two
30  Five hundred and seventy
31  Thirty-nine
32  One hundred and eighty-five point five
33  240
34  $\frac{1}{20}$
35  $\frac{9}{20}$
36  20%
37  30%
38  22
39  18
40  2
41  106
42  61
43  10 cm$^2$
44  15 cm$^2$
45  14 cm
46  22 cm
47  15
48  6
49  9
50  18

## Paper 18

1  12
2  15
3  198
4  4
5  96
6  9
7  4
8  35
9  7
10  16 m
11  16 m$^2$
12  24 cm$^2$
13  48 cm$^3$
14  12
15  22:00
16  19:30
17  11
18  18:15
19  2
20  25
21  8
22  10:05
23  94

24  54
25  88
26  2088
27  32
28  24
29  $\frac{1}{12}$
30  $\frac{1}{6}$
31  $\frac{5}{12}$
32  $\frac{1}{4}$
33  19
34  25
35  32
36  23

37–41

|        | Wholesale price | Profit (40%) | Shop price |
|--------|-----------------|--------------|------------|
| Item 1 | £6.25           | £2.50        | £8.75      |
| Item 2 | £8.50           | £3.40        | £11.90     |
| Item 3 | £12.75          | £5.10        | £17.85     |

42  23.20
43  58
44  348
45  870
46  15
47  81
48  1.25 or $1\frac{1}{4}$
49  10.75
50  4.5

## Paper 19

1  3
2  11
3  57
4  108
5  3
6  D
7  2
8  ÷
9  >
10  =
11  50
12  10
13  40
14  30
15  22

16–21

|           | Bill | Surcharge | New bill |
|-----------|------|-----------|----------|
| Mr Watt   | £160 | £12       | £172     |
| Ms Bright | £210 | £15.75    | £225.75  |
| Mrs Brass | £236 | £17.70    | £253.70  |

22  9.22
23  1.21
24  2.436
25  170
26  9000 cm$^2$
27  120 cm
28  3600 cm$^2$

29  480 cm
30  $2\frac{7}{20}$
31  $8\frac{1}{3}$
32  $9\frac{1}{3}$
33  $43\frac{1}{2}$
34  0.48
35  0.25
36  0.2
37  0.125

38–43

| ×  | 3  | 6  | 7  |
|----|----|----|----|
| 2  | 6  | 12 | 14 |
| 4  | 12 | 24 | 28 |
| 8  | 24 | 48 | 56 |

44  TRUE
45  FALSE
46  TRUE
47  TRUE

48–50

| Values |    |   |    |    | Mean of values |
|----|----|---|----|----|----------------|
| 6  | 12 | 9 | 8  | 10 | 9              |
| 15 | 17 | 13| 19 | 21 | 17             |
| 21 | 25 | 29| 23 | 27 | 25             |

## Paper 20

1  43.05
2  43.8
3  42.37
4  43.49
5–8  42.37, 43.05, 43.49, 43.8
9  $n + 5$
10  20.32
11  34
12  36
13  70
14  36
15  21
16  9
17  42

18–21

|                     | Odd | Even |
|---------------------|-----|------|
| Square number       | 9   | 36   |
| Not a square number | 21  | 42   |

22  37
23  8

24–29

Bucket of water — 1 kg
Height of a man — 200 km
Packet of sweets — 5 litres
Distance from london to Birmingham — 300 ml
Liquid in a bowl of soup — 1 m 80 cm
Weight of bag of sugar — 100 g

30  96

31 128
32 128
33 Radio 5
34 6:30 a.m.
35 9:15 p.m.
36 1:12 a.m.
37 11:59 p.m.
38 2:06 p.m.
39 5:23 p.m.
40 138.60
41 139
42 390.40
43 390
44 55.26
45 55
46 0.496
47 0.036
48 0.0111
49 0.00376
50 0.00052

## Paper 21

1 1
2 250
3 499
4 14.95
5 15.15
6 15.75
7 16.05
8 7p

9 7p
10 66p
11 $7\frac{1}{8}$
12 $4\frac{6}{7}$
13 $5\frac{1}{9}$
14 24
15 24
16 70
17 30

18–23

|  | Length | Width | Area | Perimeter |
|---|---|---|---|---|
| Rectangle 1 | 13 cm | 6 cm | **78** cm² | **38** cm |
| Rectangle 2 | **12** cm | 7 cm | 84 cm² | **38** cm |
| Rectangle 3 | 9 cm | **5** cm | 45 cm² | **28** cm |

24 71
25 12
26 6
27 24
28 3.285
29 3.16
30 42.975
31 (4, 3)
32 Lower Pasture
33 (1, 3)
34 Little Copse
35 (6, 6)

36 7
37 18
38 16
39 15
40 8
41 $4\frac{1}{4}$
42 6 tenths
43 6 units
44 6 tens
45 6 thousands

46–50

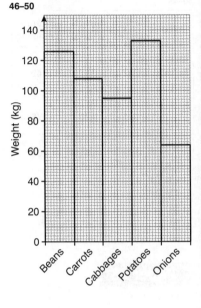

# Answers to website papers

Papers 22–24 are free to download on the Bond website. (See page iv for details). The answers to these papers are given below.

## Paper 22

1–6

|  | To nearest 1000 | To nearest 10 000 | To nearest 100 000 |
|---|---|---|---|
| 163 712 | 164 000 | 160 000 | 200 000 |
| 349 493 | 349 000 | 350 000 | 300 000 |

7 168
8 50
9 45

10 58.5
11 1.519
12 22.06
13 49.5
14 965

15–18

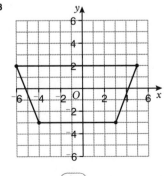

19 Trapezium
20 1
21 24
22 60
23 12
24 33
25 £3.37
26 £1.41
27 £14.97
28 £10.07
29 150
30 36%
31 18%
32 24%
33 40%

**34–36**

37 Kite
38 Isosceles triangle
39 Square

**40–45**

| Sweet | Starting number | Sweets shared | Sweets remaining |
|---|---|---|---|
| Tom thumb drops | 252 | **112** | **140** |
| Micro mints | 495 | **220** | **275** |
| Tiny tots | 369 | **164** | **205** |

46 135
47 225
48 270
49 $\frac{3}{8}$
50 $\frac{3}{4}$

## Paper 23

1 $1\frac{3}{4}$
2 $2\frac{1}{20}$
3 $10\frac{1}{8}$
4 6.375
5 1.875
6 3.225
7 £26.25
8 1001
9 26
10 39
11 52
12–13 7, 8
14 9

15 4
16 3
17 8
18–23

| × | 2 | **5** | 7 |
|---|---|---|---|
| 3 | 6 | **15** | 21 |
| 5 | 10 | 25 | **35** |
| **8** | **16** | 40 | **56** |

24 34 600
25 26 200
26 25 000
27 17 500
28 15 900

**29–34**

| | Product | Sum | Halfway |
|---|---|---|---|
| 12 and 3 | **36** | **15** | **25.5** |
| 17 and 5 | **85** | **22** | **53.5** |

35 3
36 5
37 7
38 9
39 7
40 3
41 60
42 124
43 36
44 24
45 16.5 or 16½
46 12 cm²
47 33 cm²
48 36 cm²
49 15 cm²
50 96 cm²

## Paper 24

1 994.3
2 13.1
3 785.9
4 861.9
5 17
6 18
7 57
8 18

**9–14**

| | Wholesale price | 15% | Shop price |
|---|---|---|---|
| Book A | £6.80 | £1.02 | £7.82 |
| Book B | £8.00 | £1.20 | £9.20 |
| Book C | £10.60 | £1.59 | £12.19 |

15 14:59
16 15:01
17 15:04
18 15:21
19 15:35
20 16:10
21 0.9
22 0.28
23 0.55
24 0.375
25 98
26 6
27 84
28 16
29 1050
30 $17\frac{1}{2}$
31 989.1
32 $1\frac{1}{2}$
33 0.25
34 54 cm²
35 50 cm²
36 96 cm²
37 98 cm²
38 2053.8
39 512.5
40 305.9
41 1727.1
42 30 m³
43 5
44 1.3
45 6
46 25
47 2
48 1
49 25
50 16

Josie is a scientist who counts tree rings to see how old the trees are. Each ring represents one year of the tree's life. She looked at an oak tree that was three times as old as an ash tree that was twice as old as a sycamore tree. She counted 540 rings altogether.

**17** How old was the sycamore? _____ years

**18** How old was the ash? _____ years

**19** How old was the oak? _____ years

This is a distance–time graph. It shows how far I drove my car the other day, and how long I drove for.

**20** How long did my journey take? ___ hours

**21** How long was my car stationary? ___ hours

**22–23** Between which times was I travelling the fastest? ___ : ___ and ___ : ___

Jed Irongrip plays professional golf. In a recent tournament he played four rounds of golf. Here are the scores for three of the rounds. What did he get in the fourth round?

**24** 69    72    69    ___    **Mean** average score: 71

The winner of the tournament was Blaise Fairway. He beat Jed by 8 shots (so he scored a total of 8 hits less).

**25** What was Blaise's mean average score? _____

3

B 14

B 27

4

B 15

2

Calculate these amounts of money.

B 2
B 3

**26** 49p + 37p + 18p =                                           £ _____

**27** £4.30 × 30 =                                                £ _____

**28** £15.20 + 88p + £1.75 =                                      £ _____

**29** £90.31 × 6 =                                                £ _____

5

**30** £34.50 ÷ 23 =                                               £ _____

B 26

Which numbers are the arrows are pointing to on this number line?

**31** Arrow A                                                     _____

**32** Arrow B                                                     _____

**33** Arrow C                                                     _____

**34** Arrow D                                                     _____

5

**35** Arrow E                                                     _____

Adhesive tape

£1.29

Scissors

£2.29

Stapler

£5.49

Rubber bands

£1.59

Box of staples

49p

The school secretary is buying some things for the school office. Work out what she spent on these items.

B 3
B 2

**36** Three rolls of adhesive tape.                               £ _____

**37** Two pairs of scissors.                                      £ _____

**38** A stapler and two boxes of staples.   £ _____

**39** Three boxes of rubber bands.   £ _____

**40** How much did she spend altogether?   £ _____

B 6
B 18
B 23
B 24

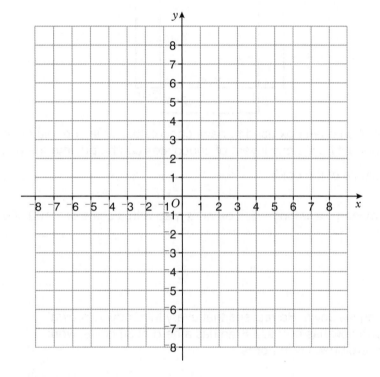

**41–43** Mark in the **coordinates** (2, ⁻3), (⁻1, 7) and (⁻4, ⁻3).

**44** Draw in the shape you have mapped.

**45** What is the shape called?   _____

**46** What is the **coordinate** of the point that lies halfway along the line of symmetry?   ( ___ , ___ )

Underline the correct answer for each of these calculations.

B 3
B 10
B 2

**47** $16 \times 12 =$   129   291   192   162

**48** $0.25 \times 6 =$   15   1.5   0.15   1.05   0.105

**49** $1.2 \times 1.2 =$   144   14.4   1.044   0.144   1.44

**50** $27 - 16.9 =$   1.01   10.1   11   9.9   0.11

*Now go to the Progress Chart to record your score!*   Total   50

# Paper 12

8 cm

8 cm

2 cm | 2 cm

1  This is the net of an open box used to pack chocolates. If the chocolates are 0.5 cm tall, work out how many layers of chocolates can be put into the box. _____

2  What is the volume of the box? _____

3  A river is 10 km long. How long will it be on a map with a scale of 1:100 000?
_____ cm

4  Stan is counting his cows. He realises that every third cow is brown and every fourth cow has horns. If Stan has a herd of 36 cows, work out how many are brown with horns. _____

Complete these sequences.

5–6  3      4      6      7      9      ___    ___

7–8  0.85    0.75    0.65    ___    ___

A temperature sensor was connected to a computer in a classroom. The temperature in the room was recorded every half an hour during the morning. This is a line graph showing temperature and the time.

 B 21
 B 22

2

B 25
B 26

1

B3/B5

1

B 7

4

B 14

**9** What was the coolest temperature? _____

**10** What time was it at its coolest? Remember to include a.m. or p.m. _____

**11** What was the warmest temperature? _____

**12** What time was it at its warmest? Remember to include a.m. or p.m. _____

**13** Put a tick next to the most likely explanation of the temperature change between 10:30 and 11:00.

☐ The sun came out.

☐ The children went out to play and left the door open.

☐ The teacher turned the heaters on.

☐ There was a total eclipse of the Sun.

5

Mr Asif made a note of the number of children who were in his science class each day for a week.

B 15

| Monday | Tuesday | Wednesday | Thursday | Friday |
|--------|---------|-----------|----------|--------|
| 23 | 28 | 27 | 28 | 29 |

**14** What is the **mode** number of children? _____

**15** What is the **range**? _____

**16** What is the **median**? _____

**17** What is the **mean**? _____

4

Marina did a survey in her school asking students which sport was their favourite. The numbers for each sport are shown in this pie chart:

B 2

B 12

B 14

Rounders

Cricket 9

18

Cross-country 45

Football 54

Netball 54

**18** How many students did she ask altogether? _____

**19** What percentage of the students chose netball? ____ %

**20** What percentage of the students chose cross-country? ____ %

**21** What percentage of the students chose rounders? ____ %

**22** What percentage of the students chose cricket? ____ %

5

Solve these calculations.

**23** $8^2 =$ _____

**24** $5^2 + 3^2 =$ _____

**25** $(2 \times 3) \times (2 \times 3) =$ _____

**26** What is 121 written as a square number? _____

**27–29** What numbers come out of this machine?

Complete these sequences.

**30–31** $\frac{1}{2}$    $\frac{2}{4}$    $\frac{3}{6}$    $\frac{4}{8}$    ____   ____

**32–33** $\frac{1}{3}$    $\frac{2}{6}$    $\frac{3}{9}$    ____   ____

**34–35** $\frac{1}{5}$    $\frac{2}{10}$    $\frac{3}{15}$    ____   ____

**36–38** What is the missing number in each of these number squares?

| 62 | 73 | 84 |
|----|----|----|
| 51 | 62 | A  |
| 40 | 51 | 62 |

A = _____

| 119 | 128 | 137 |
|-----|-----|-----|
| 110 | 119 | 128 |
| B   | 110 | 119 |

B = _____

| 33 | 48 | C  |
|----|----|----|
| 18 | 33 | 48 |
| 3  | 18 | 33 |

C = _____

At the local showground spaces were pegged out for people to put up their stalls and marquees. Here is a plan of one part of the showground:

**39** What is the perimeter of space A?

**40** What is the area of space A?

**41** What is the perimeter of space B?

**42** What is the area of space B?

**43** What is the perimeter of space C?

**44** What is the area of space C?

**45** What is the perimeter of the whole showground?

7

A car transporter has three decks, and there are three cars on each deck.

Deck A — 1060 kg    1375 kg    745 kg

Deck B — 1267 kg    1039 kg    855 kg

Deck C — 1145 kg    1220 kg    1190 kg

**46** What is the weight of the cars on Deck A?

**47** What is the weight of the cars on Deck B?

**48** What is the weight of the cars on Deck C?

**49** What is the total weight of the cars?

**50** What is the **mean** average weight of cars on Deck A?

5

*Now go to the Progress Chart to record your score!*    **Total**    50

## Paper 13

Find the answers to these calculations.

**1** $(9 \times 8) + 25 =$ _____

**2** What is this answer divided by 1000? _____

**3** $(11 \times 35) + 15 =$ _____

**4** What is this answer divided by 100? _____

**5** $(125 \div 20) + 0.50 =$ _____

**6** What is this answer divided by 10? _____

**7** $(35 \div 7) + 6.5 =$ _____

**8** What is this answer divided by 100? _____

**9** $(264 \div 22) + 7 =$ _____

**10** What is this answer divided by 1000? _____

Fill in the missing numbers.

**11** $(8 \times \text{\_\_}) + 17 = 41$

**12** $32 = (\text{\_\_} \times 2) + 6$

**13** $3 \times (56 - \text{\_\_}) = 105$

**14** $0.5 \times (8 + \text{\_\_}) = 25$

**15** $165 = 5 \times (16 + \text{\_\_})$

START

END

**16–21** The robot is on START. Describe the route the robot must take to get to the END. The robot can only move Forward, Turn Right 90° and Turn Left 90°. The first instruction has been done for you:

Forward 3, _____

_____

Janice's dad is making it easier for her to do her homework by providing her with a workspace. Work out the answers to these decisions and choices.

**22** Dad pays for the computer in three equal instalments. The computer costs £499.50. How much is each instalment?    £ _____

**23** He buys a lamp for £17.75, a wastepaper bin for £6.50, a pencil pot for £2.95 and a paper tray for £2.15. How much change will he get from £30? £ _____

**24** Dad also buys a work trolley for £59.90. For this he pays a £5 deposit and then the remaining amount in two instalments. How much is each instalment? £ _____

**25** Janice is saving for a printer costing £79. She saves £1.50 a week for 7 weeks, then £2.50 a week for 17 weeks. How much more does she need to save? £ _____

**26** DVD disks are 58p each and black printer cartridges are £4.99. Janice has £25. She buys four printer cartridges. How many disks can she buy? £ _____

**27** What is the area of this shape? _____

Underline the correct answer to each of these calculations.

**28** $46.3 + 0.75 =$     40.75     40.57     47.05     47.50     47.55

**29** $0.05 + 0.17 =$     2.2     0.22     0.022     0.202     2.02

**30** $9.2 + 3.1 + 0.25 =$ 1.255     125.5     1255     0.1255     12.55

Out of 112 children's party bags, $\frac{7}{8}$ have a moving toy inside. Of these, $\frac{3}{7}$ are jumping beetles and the rest are creeping snakes.

**31** How many contain beetles? _____

**32** How many contain snakes? _____

**33** How many contain neither? _____

Zak has entered a quiz. If he answers every question correctly, his score (which is 1 for the first question) is doubled each time.

**34** How many questions does Zak need to answer correctly to get a total of 16 points? _____

**35** How many questions does Zak need to answer correctly to get a total of 128 points? _____

**36** How many questions does Zak need to answer correctly to get a total of 256 points? _____

**37** How many questions does Zak need to answer correctly to get a total of 512 points? _____

**38–40** The dashed lines are mirror lines. Draw in the reflected shapes.

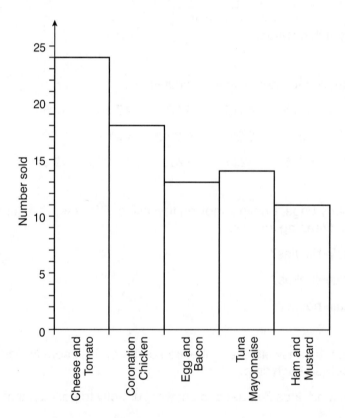

This bar chart shows the sales of sandwiches one morning in a local sandwich shop.

**41** How many sandwiches were sold altogether? _____

**42** How many coronation chicken were sold? _____

**43** How many egg and bacon, and ham and mustard were sold altogether? _____

**44** How many more cheese and tomato than tuna mayonnaise were sold? _____

T-shirt
£10.60

Sweatshirt
£18.20

Personal
CD player
£30

Pair of
socks
£2

Sports bag
£25.00

B 12

Here are the prices of five articles in a local sports outfitter.
If there was a discount of 5%, what would the prices be for the items listed below?

**45** One t-shirt                                     £ _____

**46** One sports bag                              £ _____

**47** One personal CD player                £ _____     3

If there was a discount of 15%, what would the price be for each of these items?

B 12

**48** One sweatshirt                             £ _____

**49** One pair of socks                          £ _____

**50** One t-shirt                                    £ _____     3

*Now go to the Progress Chart to record your score!*     **Total**     50

# Paper 14

**1–3** Work out the values of x, y and z in these triangles. Remember that the angles of a triangle always total 180°.

B 3
B 18

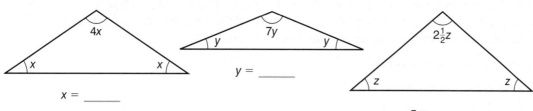

4x

x          x

x = _____

7y

y          y

y = _____

$2\frac{1}{2}z$

z          z

z = _____     3

**4–8** Fill in this timetable for Bus B using the timings for parts of the journey of Bus A to help you. Times should be written as 24-hour clock times.

|  | Bus A | Bus B |
|---|---|---|
| Pondtown | 10:35 | 11:40 |
| Wyeville | 11:07 | __ : __ |
| Avonmead | 11:33 | __ : __ |
| Severnlea | 11:48 | __ : __ |
| Wyeford | 12:06 | __ : __ |
| Pondtown | 12:39 | __ : __ |

**5**

**9** Thami bought a length of cord that measured 3 m in length. He used 1.02 m, 67 cm, 41 cm, 8.9 cm and then 26.7 cm of the cord.

How much of the cord was left? _____ cm

**10** Jo French's washing line stretches three times across her backyard. It takes 16.11 m of line to do this.

How far is it across the backyard? _____ m

**2**

A litre bottle of KERPOW washing-up liquid costs £1.95.

**11** How much would a five-litre bottle of KERPOW cost? £ _____

**12** If I use 10 ml to wash my pots each time, how many pot washes can I do from a five-litre bottle before I need a new one? _____

**13** How much will 20 pot washes cost ? _____ p

**3**

KERPOW is also sold in 500 ml and 250 ml bottles. They cost £1.05 and 60p respectively.

**14** How much more would it cost me to buy four 500 ml bottles than two 1-litre bottles? _____ p

**15** How much more would it cost me to buy four 250 ml bottles rather than a litre bottle? _____ p

**2**

At the local fire station they have different lengths of fire hose. The shortest is half the length of the middle-sized one, and one fifth of the length of the longest one. If I connect the three different hose lengths together I make a hose 120 m long.

**16** How long is the shortest hose? _____ m

**17** How long is the middle hose? _____ m

**18** How long is the longest hose? _____ m

**3**

Calculate the perimeter and area of each of these rectangles.

**19–20** Rectangle A has a perimeter of _____ cm, and an area of _____ cm².

**21–22** Rectangle B has a perimeter of _____ cm, and an area of _____ cm².

**23–24** Rectangle C has a perimeter of _____ cm, and an area of _____ cm².

**25–31** Write these numbers in the appropriate sections of this Venn diagram.

9    35    10    105

14    15    21

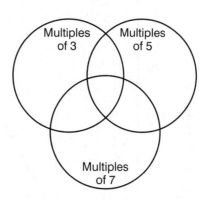

**32** If Naveen is $p$ years old in 2 years' time what was her age 6 years ago? _____ years

Find the answers to these calculations.

**33** $496.07 - 219.88 =$ _____

**34** $1792\frac{1}{2} + 40\frac{1}{10} =$ _____

**35** $31.5 \div 7 =$ _____

**36** $905 \times 43 =$ _____

Calculate these amounts of money.

**37** $503p + £27.99 =$ £ _____

**38** $£7.60 \times 8 =$ £ _____

**39** $\frac{1}{8}$ of £13.60 $=$ £ _____

**40** $£43.05 - 15p =$ £ _____

Work out what number the letter represents in each of these equations.

**41** 6a + 7 = 25                                         a = ____

**42** 3b × 6 = 72                                         b = ____

**43** 8c ÷ 4 = 12                                         c = ____

Now use the values you have found for a, b and c to find the solution to this equation.

**44** (5a × 2b) − 10c =                                   ____

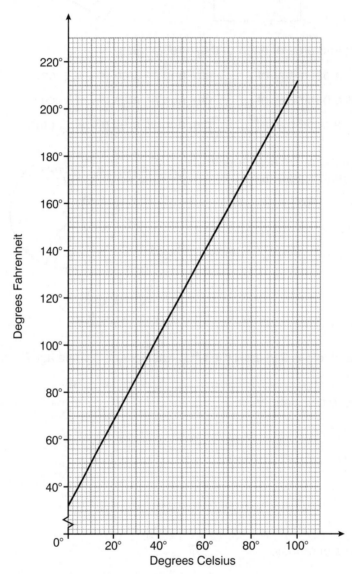

Use this temperature conversion graph to convert these temperatures.

**45** 75°C → _____ °F                    **46** 50°C → _____ °F

**47** 15°C → _____ °F                    **48** 212°F → _____ °C

**49** 41°F → _____ °C                    **50** 68°F → _____ °C

*Now go to the Progress Chart to record your score!*     Total     50

# Paper 15

Solve these calculations, writing your answers as numbers.

B1/B2
B 3

1 Add one hundred and five to seventy-four. _____

2 What is the sum of two point five two and one point three five? _____

3 Find the difference between three hundred and seventy-five and two hundred and ninety-eight. _____

4 Subtract fifteen point nine seven from twenty-six point one two. _____

5 Multiply eleven point nine by sixty. _____

6 What are seventy lots of nine point seven? _____

7 How many twelves go into one hundred and ninety-two? _____

8 Divide four hundred and fourteen by twenty-three. _____

8

Complete these sequences.

B 7

9–10  12.25   12.50   12.75   ____   ____

11–12  $\frac{1}{2}$   $\frac{1}{4}$   $\frac{1}{8}$   $\frac{1}{16}$   ____   ____

13–14  16   17   19   22   ____   ____

6

15–20 Fill in the missing values in this table of different-sized rectangles.

B 20

| | Length | Width | Perimeter | Area |
|---|---|---|---|---|
| Rectangle 1 | 6 cm | 4 cm | _____ cm | _____ cm² |
| Rectangle 2 | 9 cm | _____ cm | 24 cm | _____ cm² |
| Rectangle 3 | _____ cm | 6 cm | _____ cm | 66 cm² |

6

21–24 In my local travel shop I can exchange Euros for British pounds when I come back from holiday. I get £1 for every 1.46 Euros. Complete this table for different values of Euros that people exchanged in front of me in the shop.

B3/B13

| Euros | Pounds |
|---|---|
| €14.60 | £ _____ |
| €109.50 | £ _____ |
| €73 | £ _____ |
| €365 | £ _____ |

4

Calculate the **mean** and **range** of each of these sets of numbers.

**25–26** 22    15    18    23    17        Range ____ Mean ____

**27–28** 106   112   110   112        Range ____ Mean ____

**29–30** 36    29    35    38    36    30    Range ____ Mean ____

B 15

6

B 20

**31** If each of the small triangles shown has an area of $y^2$, what is the area of the star? ____

1

Mrs Tilley keeps a variety of poultry. This pie chart shows the numbers of each kind:

B 14

B 12

B 10

27 Geese

45 Turkeys

72 Hens

36 Ducks

**32** What percentage of the poultry are hens? ____ %

**33** What percentage of the poultry are geese? ____ %

**34** What fraction of the poultry are ducks? ____

**35** What fraction of the poultry are turkeys? ____

4

Here are some of the numbers that were picked out of the bag at a bingo evening.

20    32    95    16    18    31    24    17

B 6

**36** Which of these numbers is a square number? ____

**37–38** Which of these numbers are **prime numbers**? ____ and ____

3

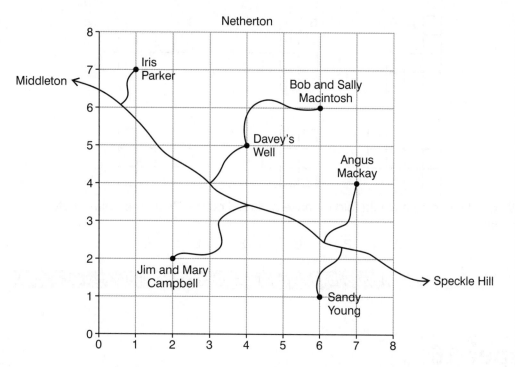

Netherton

Netherton, on the Isle of Bacon, is a small hamlet with only a few houses. This map shows Netherton.

**39–41** Who lives at these **coordinates**?

(1, 7) _____

(6, 1) _____

(6, 6) _____

**42–43** What are the **coordinates** of these people's homes?

Angus Mackay  ( ___ , ___ )

Jim and Mary Campbell  ( ___ , ___ )

**44** Which family has to pass the ancient Davey's Well to get to the main road?

_____

6

Badia is the apprentice at the local screws and nails factory. The other day she made some six-inch nails. Charli who works next to her made one and half times as many as Badia, but Siva made twice as many as Charli. They all made a total of 110 six-inch nails.

**45** How many did Badia make? _____

**46** How many did Charli make? _____

**47** How many did Siva make? _____

3

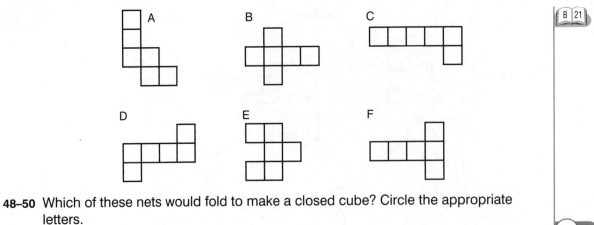

**48–50** Which of these nets would fold to make a closed cube? Circle the appropriate letters.

A    B    C    D    E    F

*Now go to the Progress Chart to record your score!*   Total   50

# Paper 16

Find the three **prime factors** for each given number.

**1–3** $30 = $ \_\_ $\times$ \_\_ $\times$ \_\_

**4–6** $110 = $ \_\_ $\times$ \_\_ $\times$ \_\_

**7–9** $165 = $ \_\_ $\times$ \_\_ $\times$ \_\_

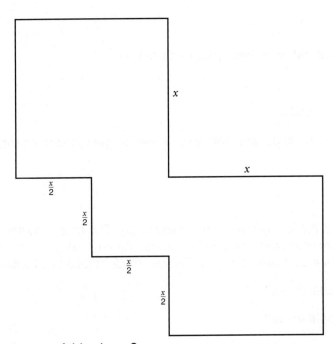

## 9

**10** What is the perimeter of this shape?  _____

Underline the correct answer for each of these calculations.

**11**  $636 \div 12 =$      5.3      50.3      35      53      530

**12**  $\frac{1}{7} + \frac{4}{21} =$      $\frac{7}{21}$      $\frac{5}{21}$      $\frac{5}{7}$      $\frac{5}{28}$      $\frac{7}{28}$

**13**  What % of 65 is 13?      30%      25%      20%      15%      10%

**14**  $2.05 - 0.15 =$      1.009      9.01      9.1      1.09      1.9

Multiply these numbers by 100.

**15**  0.27  _____

**16**  0.035  _____

**17**  0.101  _____

Divide these numbers by 1000.

**18**  659  _____

**19**  38  _____

**20**  1.65  _____

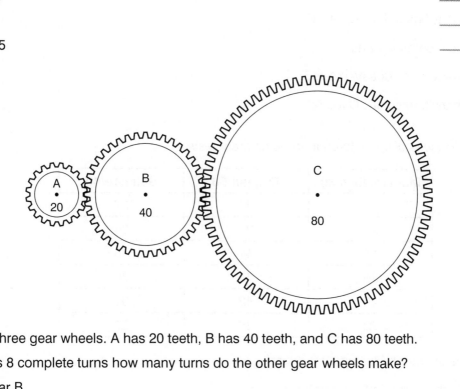

Here are three gear wheels. A has 20 teeth, B has 40 teeth, and C has 80 teeth.

If A makes 8 complete turns how many turns do the other gear wheels make?

**21**  Gear B  _____

**22**  Gear C  _____

If A made just one complete turn what fraction of a turn would each of the other gear wheels make?

**23**  Gear B  _____

**24**  Gear C  _____

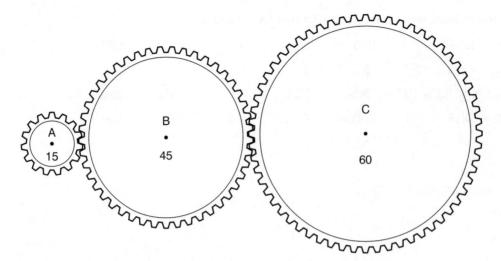

Here are three more gear wheels. In this arrangement A has 15 teeth, B has 45 teeth, and C has 60 teeth. If A makes four complete turns: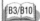

    **25** how many times does B rotate?     ____

    **26** how many times does C rotate?     ____

If B makes four complete turns:

    **27** how many times does A rotate?     ____

    **28** how many times does C rotate?     ____    ◯ 4

These are the results of six children in three different tests:    B 15

| Mathematics/30 | English/50 | Science/40 |
|:---:|:---:|:---:|
| 16 | 31 | 27 |
| 23 | 32 | 25 |
| 14 | 41 | 28 |
| 26 | 44 | 30 |
| 25 | 42 | 31 |
| 22 | 38 | 27 |

**29** What is the **mean** Mathematics score?     ____

**30** What is the **range** in Mathematics scores?     ____

**31** What is the **mean** English score?     ____

**32** What is the **range** in English scores?     ____

**33** What is the **mean** Science score?     ____

**34** What is the **range** in Science scores?     ____    ◯ 6

Pack of low
energy light bulbs
£4.29

Tin of paint
£7.99

Extension lead
£4.49

Pack of spotlights
£7.90

These are some of the prices at my DIY store. Use the prices to work out the answers to these money problems.

B4/B2
B 3

**35** What change would I get from £20 if I bought 2 extension leads and 1 pack of spotlights? £ _____

**36** What change would I get from £40 if I bought 2 packs of low energy light bulbs and 3 tins of paint? £ _____

**37** What change would I get from £30 if I bought 1 pack of spotlights and 4 packs of low energy light bulbs? £ _____

**38** What change would I get from £25 if I bought one of each item? _____ p

8 m · 21 m · 1 m

B 20

Here is a plan of Bill's allotment. He divides it into four equal sized plots and all of his paths are one metre wide. Use this information and what you can see on the plan to work out the answers to these questions.

**39** What is the perimeter of the whole allotment? ___ m

**40** What is the area of each plot? ___ m²

**41** What is the perimeter of each plot? ___ m

**42** What is the area of the part of the path that goes around the edge of the allotment? ___ m²

**43–46** Put these values in order from largest to smallest.

$\frac{17}{50}$    23%    $\frac{2}{3}$    78%    _____,  _____,  _____,  _____

B10/B12

**47**

**48**

**49**

**50**

Using the terms tetrahedron, square-based pyramid, cuboid and open-topped cube, label each net above to show what 3-D shape it would make.

*Now go to the Progress Chart to record your score!*   Total   50

# Paper 17

Solve these calculations.

**1** $3.8 \times 6 =$ _____

**2** $9.24 \times 7 =$ _____

**3** $7.6 \times 8 =$ _____

**4** $8.51 \times 5 =$ _____

Solve these calculations.

**5** $289 \div 8.5 =$ _____

**6** $304 \div 1.6 =$ _____

**7** $89.6 \div 28 =$ _____

**8** $32.2 \div 1.4 =$ _____

Put the appropriate sign $<$, $>$ or $=$ in these calculations.

**9** $(6 \times 3.1)$ ___ $(10 + 9)$

**10** $(8 + 6.4)$ ___ $(7.2 \times 2)$

**11** $(3 \times 3)$ ___ $(2 \times 2 \times 2)$

**12** $(4^2 - 3^2)$ ___ $(3.5 \times 2)$

**13** $(7.1 \times 5)$ ___ $6^2$

B 21

4

B11/B3

4

B11/B3

4

A 6

B3/B2

B2/B3

B 3

B6/B3

B3/B6

5

**14–19** Here is a recipe for making apple flapjacks. Convert the imperial units to metric units. Remember that 1 ounce (oz) is approximately 25 grams (g) and 1 pound (lb) is approximately 16 ounces (oz).

| Apple Flapjacks | |
|---|---|
| IMPERIAL | METRIC |
| 2 level tablespoons of golden syrup | 2 level tablespoons of golden syrup |
| 2 oz margarine | _____ g margarine |
| 3 oz demerara sugar | _____ g demerara sugar |
| 6 oz rolled oats | _____ g rolled oats |
| FILLING | |
| $1\frac{1}{5}$ oz margarine | _____ g margarine |
| 1 lb cooking apples | _____ g cooking apples |
| $2\frac{2}{5}$ oz granulated sugar | _____ g granulated sugar |

Work out what the letters $x$, $y$ and $z$ stand for in each of these equations.

**20** $9x - 12 = 42$ $\qquad\qquad x =$ ____

**21** $3y \div 2 = 12$ $\qquad\qquad y =$ ____

**22** $6z + 30 = 48$ $\qquad\qquad z =$ ____

Now use the values that you have found for $x$, $y$ and $z$ to calculate the areas and perimeters of these rectangles.

A   B   C

**23–24** Rectangle A has an area of _____ cm² and a perimeter of _____ cm.

**25–26** Rectangle B has an area of _____ cm² and a perimeter of _____ cm.

**27–28** Rectangle C has an area of _____ cm² and a perimeter of _____ cm.

Find the answers to these calculations, writing your answer for each one in words.

**29** $28 + 17 + 92 + 35 =$ _____

**30** $109 + 151 + 106 + 204 =$ _____

**31** $6.5 + 9.25 + 3.75 + 19.5 =$ _____

**32** $30.6 + 28 + 70.4 + 56.5 =$ _____

_____

Dwayne collects stamps from four different countries. This table shows the number he has from each country.

B2/B10
B 12

| USA | Canada | Australia | New Zealand |
|---|---|---|---|
| 108 | 72 | 48 | 12 |

**33** How many stamps does Dwayne have in total? _____

**34** What fraction of these (in lowest terms) are from New Zealand? _____

**35** What fraction of these (in lowest terms) are from the USA? _____

**36** What percentage of these are from Australia? _____

**37** What percentage of these are from Canada? _____

**5**

Round these figures to the nearest whole number.

B 1

**38** 21.6 _____

**39** 18.39 _____

**40** 1.71 _____

**41** 106.449 _____

**42** 60.81 _____

**5**

A sign-writer designed this stamp for boxes to show which way up they should be kept. All the letters are 1 cm wide.

B20/B3

**43** What is the area of the letter T? _____

**44** What is the area of the letter P? _____

**45** What is the perimeter of the space in the centre of the letter O? _____

**46** What is the perimeter of the outside of the letter P? _____

To design the stamp the sign-writer painted an example first. Every 3 cm² took one brush-load of paint.

B20/B2
B 3

**47** How many times did he load up the brush to paint TOP? _____

**5**

At the local vegetable show Cruz, Seth and Joanna entered marrows in the largest marrow competition. Joanna's was $1\frac{1}{2}$ times as heavy as Seth's, and Cruz's was twice as heavy as Joanna's. The total weight of the three marrows was 33 lb.

B 13

**48** What was the weight of Seth's marrow? _____ lb

**49** What was the weight of Joanna's marrow? _____ lb

**50** What was the weight of Cruz's marrow? _____ lb

**3**

## Paper 18

Fill in the missing numbers in these calculations.

**1** 23 × ___ = 276

**2** ___ × 21 = 315

**3** 18 × 11 = ___

**4** 37 × ___ = 148

**5** ___ × 20 = 1920

Tariq kept a record of the number of hours he spent watching TV each week for 6 weeks. Here is what he recorded.

|   |   |   |   |   |   |
|---|---|---|---|---|---|
| 7 | 9 | 11 | 8 | 10 | 9 |

**6** What is the **mean** number of hours? ___

**7** What is the **range**? ___

Nini counted the number of skips she could do before she tripped. Here are her results for several tries.

|   |   |   |   |   |   |   |
|---|---|---|---|---|---|---|
| 35 | 38 | 34 | 33 | 37 | 37 | 31 |

**8** What is the **mean** number of skips? ___

**9** What is the **range**? ___

**10** Chen-chi watched a snail take 2 hours to go round the edge of her patio. If the snail travelled 8 metres every hour, what is the perimeter of her patio? ___

**11** If her patio is square what is its area? ___

**12** This diagram shows the net of a tin. What is the area of the lid? ___ cm²

**13** What is the volume of the tin? ___ cm³

**14** Three years ago Ravi had 2 collectable trains. Every year since he has bought 2 more trains. Calculate how many collectable trains Ravi will have in 2 years' time. ___

**12:00** London UK
 **15:00** Moscow Russia
 **04:00** San Francisco USA
 **20:00** Perth Australia
**09:00** Rio de Janeiro Brazil

While it might be 12:00 in London, the digital clocks in other places show that the time there is different. Use the clocks shown here to answer these questions.

**15** When it is 14:00 in London, what time will it be in Perth? ___ : ___

**16** When it is 16:30 in Rio de Janeiro, what time will it be in London? ___ : ___

**17** It is the same day in Moscow and San Francisco.
What is the difference in hours between the clocks? ___ hours

**18** When it is 23:15 in Perth, what time will it be in Moscow? ___ : ___

 4

|  | OUT | RETURN |
|---|---|---|
| Great Summerfield | 08:15 | 10:13 |
| Little Summerfield | 08:23 | 10:05 |
| Edgeton | 08:33 | 09:53 |
| Leaside | 08:41 | 09:44 |
| Bridgeville | 08:48 | 09:37 |
| Malmington | 08:56 | 09:30 |

This is part of the timetable for a local village bus service. Use it to answer these questions.

**19** How much longer does it take to get from Malmington to
Great Summerfield than Great Summerfield to Malmington? ___ minutes

**20** How long does it take to travel from Little Summerfield to Bridgeville? ___ minutes

**21** How long does it take to travel from Little Summerfield to
Great Summerfield? ___ minutes

**22** One morning the bus was delayed at Bridgeville for 12 minutes.
What time did it arrive at Edgeton? ___ : ___

4

I received this parcel of books yesterday. After I had emptied it I opened it out flat for recycling.

B 20

B 21

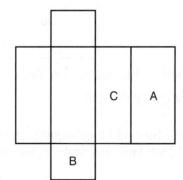

**23** What is the perimeter of face A? _____ cm

**24** What is the perimeter of face B? _____ cm

**25** What is the perimeter of face C? _____ cm

**26** What is the total area of the flattened box? _____ cm² ◯ 4

There are four strawberry crèmes to every three raspberry whirls in a box of chocolates. B 13
There are fifty-six chocolates altogether.

**27–28** There are ____ strawberry crèmes and ____ raspberry whirls. ◯ 2

B 10

**29–32** What proportion of the large rectangle (in **lowest terms**) is each of the smaller shapes?

A _____

B _____

C _____

D _____ ◯ 4

Solve these calculations. B 3

**33** 304 ÷ 16 = _____

**34** 450 ÷ 18 = _____

**35** 896 ÷ 28 = _____

**36** 322 ÷ 14 = _____ ◯ 4

**37–41** Debbie, who runs the village shop, went to the wholesalers to buy some things to B12/B2
sell in the shop. She adds 40% to the wholesale price to work out what the price
in the shop will be. Complete this table.

|  | Wholesale price | Profit (40%) | Shop price |
|---|---|---|---|
| Item 1 | £6.25 | £2.50 | £ _____ |
| Item 2 | £8.50 | £ _____ | £ _____ |
| Item 3 | £12.75 | £ _____ | £ _____ |

◯ 5

**42–45** The exchange rate for Trinidad and Tobago dollars is 11.6 dollars ($) to the British pound (£). Complete this table.

| British pounds (£) | Trinidad and Tobago dollars ($) |
|:---:|:---:|
| 2 | _____ |
| 5 | _____ |
| 30 | _____ |
| 75 | _____ |

**4**

Determine the value of each of the letters in these equations.

**46** $\dfrac{a}{25} = 60\%$  $\qquad\qquad\qquad\qquad\qquad a =$ ___

**47** $\dfrac{b}{108} = \dfrac{3}{4}$  $\qquad\qquad\qquad\qquad\qquad b =$ ___

**48** $4 \times c = 5$  $\qquad\qquad\qquad\qquad\qquad c =$ ___

**49** $d + 6.5 = 17.25$  $\qquad\qquad\qquad\qquad d =$ ___

**50** $\dfrac{(e + 3.5)}{40} = 20\%$  $\qquad\qquad\qquad\quad e =$ ___

**5**

*Now go to the Progress Chart to record your score!*  **Total**  **50**

## Paper 19

Fill in the missing numbers in these calculations.

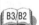

**1** $(8 \times \underline{\quad}) + 17 = 41$  $\qquad\qquad$ **2** $28 = (\underline{\quad} \times 2) + 6$

**3** $4 \times (66 - \underline{\quad}) = 36$  $\qquad\qquad$ **4** $(\underline{\quad} \div 9) - 6 = 6$

**5** $(36 \div \underline{\quad}) + 80 = 92$

**5**

**6** Which of the following shapes has an area of 8 cm²? Circle the appropriate letter.

   A  a square with sides of 4 cm

   B  a triangle with a base of 2 cm and a height of 2 cm

   C  a triangle with a base of 2 cm and a height 4 cm

   D  a rectangle with sides of 2 cm and 4 cm

**1**

**7** The **mean** of the following 10 numbers is 2.4. Find the missing number.

   2  6  1  2  3  ___  2  1  4  1

**1**

Put the correct sign $<$, $>$, $=$, $\div$, $\times$ in these calculations.

**8** 405 ___ 27 = 15

**9** (3.5 $\times$ 3) ___ 7.5 + 2.75

**10** (3 + 3 + 3 + 3 + 3) ___ (45 $\div$ 3)

3

Turn these fractions into percentages.

B 10

B 12

**11** $\frac{17}{34}$ = ___ %          **12** $\frac{9}{90}$ = ___ %

**13** $\frac{28}{70}$ = ___ %          **14** $\frac{36}{120}$ = ___ %

**15** $\frac{55}{250}$ = ___ %

5

**16–21** The Zap Electricity Company has added $7\frac{1}{2}$% surcharge to its bills. Complete this table for the surcharge and new bills for three of their customers.

B12/B2

|  | Bill | Surcharge | New bill |
|---|---|---|---|
| Mr Watt | £160 | £ _____ | £ _____ |
| Ms Bright | £210 | £ _____ | £ _____ |
| Mrs Brass | £236 | £ _____ | £ _____ |

6

Find the answers to these calculations.

B2/B25

B 3

**22** 11.97 km − 2.75 km =                    _____ km

**23** 3976 cm − 38.55 m =                    _____ m

**24** 6 $\times$ 406 m =                    _____ km

**25** 5.78 km $\div$ 34 =                    _____ m

4

A carpenter is making an outdoor game for his children. He draws a diagram showing where he should saw a sheet of plywood.

B 20

**26** What is the area of part A?          _____

**27** What is the perimeter of part B?          _____

**28** What is the area of part C?          _____

**29** What is the perimeter of the whole sheet of plywood?          _____

4

Turn these fractions into **mixed numbers** in their **lowest terms**.

**30** $\frac{47}{20} =$ _____     **31** $\frac{125}{15} =$ _____     **32** $\frac{28}{3} =$ _____     **33** $\frac{174}{4} =$ _____

Turn these fractions into decimals.

**34** $\frac{12}{25} =$ _____     **35** $\frac{6}{24} =$ _____     **36** $\frac{17}{85} =$ _____     **37** $\frac{6}{48} =$ _____

**38–43** Insert the missing numbers to complete this multiplication table.

| × | ___ | ___ | ___ |
|---|---|---|---|
| ___ | 6 | 12 | 14 |
| ___ | 12 | 24 | 28 |
| ___ | 24 | 48 | 56 |

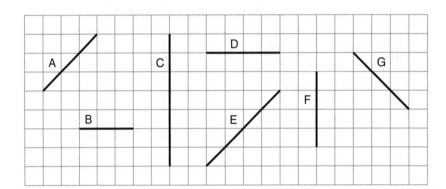

Circle TRUE or FALSE for each of these statements.

**44** Line F is a vertical line.     TRUE     FALSE

**45** Line G is perpendicular to D.     TRUE     FALSE

**46** Line A is parallel to E.     TRUE     FALSE

**47** Line B is perpendicular to C.     TRUE     FALSE

**48–50** Fill in the missing numbers in this table.

| Values | | | | | Mean of values |
|---|---|---|---|---|---|
| 6 | 12 | ___ | 8 | 10 | 9 |
| 15 | 17 | 13 | 19 | ___ | 17 |
| 21 | 25 | 29 | 23 | 27 | ___ |

## Paper 20

Find out the answers to these calculations.

    **1** $1.6 + 38.2 + 3.25 =$ _____      **2** $0.15 + 30.05 + 13.6 =$ _____

    **3** $31.6 + 0.45 + 10.32 =$ _____      **4** $20.05 + 21.75 + 1.69 =$ _____

  **5–8** Using the answers you have just found, order them from smallest to largest.

_____     _____     _____     _____

   **9** Melly was $n$ years old last year. How old will she be in 4 years' time? _____ years

  **10** Here is a table showing the conversion of inches to centimetres.
Fill in the missing conversion.

| Inches | Centimetres |
|:------:|:-----------:|
| 7 | 17.78 |
| 8 | _____ |
| 9 | 22.86 |
| 10 | 25.40 |

A car manufacturer has parked some new cars in two car parks. In the first car park there are 60 cars in the ratio 1 red car for every 2 blue cars and 3 silver cars. In the second car park there are 80 cars in the ratio 2 blue cars for every 3 red cars and 5 silver cars.

  **11** How many red cars are there altogether? _____

  **12** How many blue cars are there altogether? _____

  **13** How many silver cars are there altogether? _____

Calculate the values that the letters $a$, $b$, $c$, and $d$ represent.

  **14** $a = 7^2 - 13$      $a =$ ___      **15** $b = (3.5 \times 12) \div 2$      $b =$ ___

  **16** $c = (45 - 9) \div 4$      $c =$ ___      **17** $d = (40\%$ of $840) \div 8$      $d =$ ___

 **18–21** Now write the values that you have found in this table.

|  | Odd | Even |
|---|:---:|:---:|
| Square number | ___ | ___ |
| Not a square number | ___ | ___ |

These were my scores at a local skittles evening.

           33      37      39      41      34      38

  **22** What was my **mean** score? ___

  **23** What was the **range** of my scores? ___

**24–29** Draw lines to connect the items on the left to their possible dimensions on the right.

B 25

| | |
|---|---|
| Bucket of water | 1 kg |
| Height of a man | 200 km |
| Packet of sweets | 5 litres |
| Distance from London to Birmingham | 300 ml |
| Liquid in a bowl of soup | 1 m 80 cm |
| Weight of a bag of sugar | 100 g |

6

640 people were asked which BBC Radio station they preferred to listen to. This pie chart shows the results:

B 14
B 12
B 2

**30** How many people prefer Radio 1? _____

**31** How many people prefer Radio 4? _____

**32** How many more people prefer Radio 2 than Radio 3? _____

**33** Which radio station attracts as many listeners as Radio 1 and Radio 3 together? _____

Radio 1 15%
Radio 2 30%
Radio 3 10%
Radio 4 20%
Radio 5 25%

4

**34–39** Complete this table converting the digital clock times to a 12-hour clock time.

B 27

| Digital time | 12-hour clock time |
|---|---|
| 06:30 | _____ |
| 21:15 | _____ |
| 01:12 | _____ |
| 23:59 | _____ |
| 14:06 | _____ |
| 17:23 | _____ |

6

Calculate the answers to these money problems, and then round your answer to the nearest pound.

B3/B1

**40–41** £4.62 × 30 = £ _____ which is £ _____ to the nearest pound.

**42–43** £9.76 × 40 = £ _____ which is £ _____ to the nearest pound.

**44–45** £6.14 × 9 = £ _____ which is £ _____ to the nearest pound.

6

Divide these numbers by 1000.

B 1

**46** 496 _____    **47** 36 _____    **48** 11.1 _____

**49** 3.76 _____    **50** 0.52 _____

5

*Now go to the Progress Chart to record your score!*    Total    50

## Paper 21

Find the answer to each of these problems.

1 In a leap year how many more days are there in May, June and July combined, than in January, February and March combined? _____

2 I enjoy making curry. The recipe that I like most uses two tablespoons of oil. There are 15 ml in a tablespoon. From a full bottle I can make 8 curries but I find that I have 10 ml of oil left over. How much oil is there in a full bottle? _____ ml

3 A local computer shop has a deal on a new computer that I would like to buy. They want a deposit of £115 and then 6 payments of £64. How much will the computer cost me?  £ _____

4–7 Which numbers are the arrows pointing to on this number line?

Arrow A _____  Arrow B _____  Arrow C _____  Arrow D _____

A local shop has these packs of paper for sale.

50 sheets
75p

75 sheets
£1.05

100 sheets
£1.28

250 sheets
£3.25

8 If I want 150 sheets, what is the difference in price between buying one pack of 50 sheets plus one pack of 100 sheets, and buying two 75-sheet packs? _____ p

9 One day they had sold out of the 250-sheet packs. What is the difference in price between buying 2 packs of 75 sheets plus a 100-sheet pack, and buying 2 packs of 100 sheets plus a 50-sheet pack? _____ p

10 What is the difference between the cost of 6 packs of 50 sheets and 3 packs of 100 sheets? _____ p

Convert these **improper fractions** to **mixed numbers** in their **lowest terms**.

11 $\frac{57}{8}$ _____    12 $\frac{34}{7}$ _____    13 $\frac{46}{9}$ _____

In each row there is a number that can be divided exactly by each of the first pair or group of numbers given. Circle this number in each row.

 B 5

| 14 | 3 and 8 | 12 | 16 | 24 | 30 | 36 |
| 15 | 6 and 12 | 18 | 24 | 30 | 42 | 50 |
| 16 | 2 and 5 and 7 | 40 | 50 | 60 | 70 | 80 |
| 17 | 3 and 6 and 5 | 12 | 18 | 30 | 36 | 49 |

 4

18–23 Complete this table.

 B 20

|  | **Length** | **Width** | **Area** | **Perimeter** |
|---|---|---|---|---|
| Rectangle 1 | 13 cm | 6 cm | ___ cm² | ___ cm |
| Rectangle 2 | ___ cm | 7 cm | 84 cm² | ___ cm |
| Rectangle 3 | 9 cm | ___ cm | 45 cm² | ___ cm |

 6

24 Test tubes are sold in packs of four. A local technology college needs 282 test tubes. How many packs will they need to buy? _____

 B 3

 1

There were 42 people who went on my class trip. Two sevenths of them were parents, and one seventh were teachers. The remainder were pupils.

 B 10

B 13

25 How many parents were there? _____

26 How many teachers were there? _____

27 How many pupils were there? _____

 3

Work out the answers to these calculations.

B 2

28 0.175 + 2.5 + 0.61 = _____

B 11

29 1.09 + 1.63 + 0.44 = _____

30 15.6 + 14.25 + 13.125 = _____

 3

31 What are the **coordinates** of Mr Adam's farm?

( ___ , ___ )

32 What place lies west of Mr Adam's farm?

_____

33 What are its **coordinates**? ( ___ , ___ )

34 What place is south-east of Mr Adam's farm?

_____

35 What are the **coordinates** of the building north of this place? ( ___ , ___ )

 B 23

 5

Here are some mathematics test results of nine children in Year 6. The test was out of 20.

16    18    14    18    12    16    11    18    12

**36** What is the **range**?    ___

**37** What is the **mode**?    ___

**38** What is the **median**?    ___

**39** What is the **mean**?    ___    4

Complete these sequences.

B7/B10

**40** 3.5    5    6.5    ___    9.5

**41** $\frac{1}{2}$    $1\frac{3}{4}$    3    ___    $5\frac{1}{2}$    2

What is the value of number 6 in each of these figures?    B 1

**42** 1.65    _____    **43** 16.03 _____

**44** 162.54 _____    **45** 6023 _____    4

**46–50** A local smallholder weighs all of his crops when he picks them. Here are the weights of five of the crops. Draw a bar chart to show these.    B 14

126 kilograms of beans,
108 kilograms of carrots,
 95 kilograms of cabbages,
133 kilograms of potatoes,
 64 kilograms of onions.

*Now go to the Progress Chart to record your score!*    Total    50

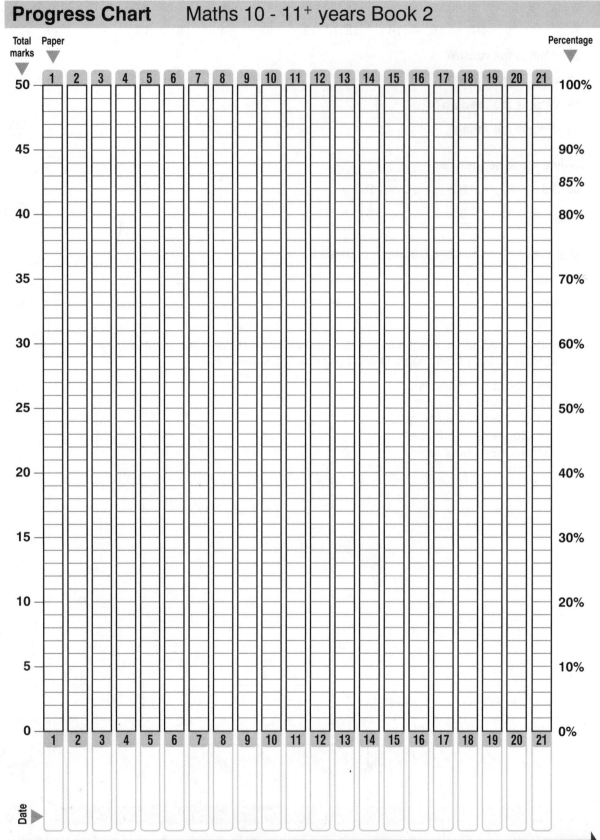

# Progress Chart     Maths 10 - 11⁺ years Book 2

When you've finished the book use the Next Steps Planner